ADVANCED

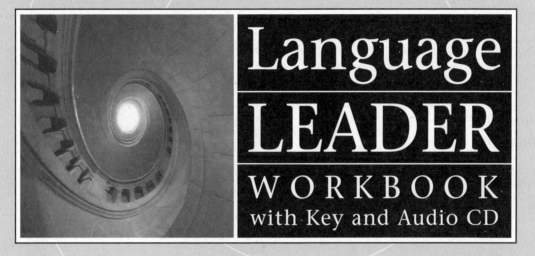

Language
LEADER
WORKBOOK
with Key and Audio CD

PEARSON
Longman

Grant Kempton

CONTENTS

LANGUAGE LEADER ADVANCED

CONTENTS

Listening	Scenario	Study & Writing skills
Explanations of educational terms Short interviews DICTATION Interview	Choosing an intern Key language: stating requirements; saying what is essential and desirable	A covering letter
DICTATION Radio programme A meeting	Granville Island Key language: stating your position clarifying	Planning and organising essays Problem-solution essay
DICTATION Discussion Lecture	The oil spill crisis Key language: stating objectives; giving strong advice	Active listening Writing a speech
Radio debate LISTEN BETTER: inference DICTATION Conversation	Change your ways! Key language: justifying your opinions	Analysing visual information Describing visual information
A news item DICTATION Interviews	Retail revamp Key language: discussing hypothetical ideas	Reading complex texts effectively Summarising WRITE BETTER: Plagiarism
Lecture A talk	A radio debate Key language: using persuasive language and giving examples	TRANSLATION Writing a sales leaflet Advanced dictionary skills
DICTATION Discussion Radio programme	Camomila Key language: approving ideas, raising doubt, objections	Critical thinking WRITE/SPEAK BETTER: stating a point, elaborating, giving examples An opinion-lead essay WRITE BETTER: sticking to the point
DICTATION Interview Conversation	Sailing close to the wind Key language: being cautious	Research skills Writing a features article for a magazine or newspaper
A talk DICTATION	Law makers Sailing close to the wind Key language: balancing an argument	Synthesising information A literature review
DICTATION Lecture Panel discussion	Reality Island Key language: an informal talk	Seminar / discussion skills Creative writing (a screenplay) WRITE BETTER: turning a narrative into a screenplay
Conversation DICTATION A talk	Ariel capital Key language: setting the agenda and responding to offers	Making a business presentation A tactful business email
Interviews DICTATION A talk Lecture	Ask the panel Key language: referring to what other people have said	Examination skills A personal statement

LANGUAGE LEADER ADVANCED

1 Education and employment

1.1 ISSUES IN EDUCATION

1 Reorder the letters to make words and phrases connected with education.

1 mudbing wond   _____

2 sassenemts   _____

3 pretinsonlaer slliks   _____

4 ismplagari   _____

5 mulcurcirlu   _____

6 gimnstrea   _____

7 litesmi   _____

LISTENING

2 `1.2` **Listen to some university professors explaining the words and phrases in Exercise 1. Label each excerpt with the words and phrases from Exercise 1.**

1 _____   5 _____

2 _____   6 _____

3 _____   7 _____

4 _____

TRANSLATION

3 Translate these idiomatic expressions that describe character into your own language.

1 all-rounder   _____

2 dark horse   _____

3 high-flier   _____

4 know-all   _____

5 loose cannon   _____

6 whizz kid   _____

VOCABULARY: idioms

4 Match four of the idiomatic expressions in Exercise 3 with the character descriptions 1–4.

1 With Jane you never really can tell what she's going to do. She's quite capable of starting an argument with Paul over money, even shouting and screaming at him. _____

2 Khaled is one of those annoying people who succeeded at everything at school – sports, science, music – there's nothing he's not pretty good at.
_____

3 Watch Penelope closely over the next few years. She's well on the way to getting a scholarship and in no time at all she'll probably be the CEO of a multinational. _____

4 Everyone thinks they know what the result will be, but don't write off Tad. He's been working very hard behind the scenes and although everyone else would be surprised, I think he has a really good chance. _____

READING

1 Read the following text and fill the gaps with the correct headings.

A They solve problems rather than place blame.

B They rehearse the future as they see it.

C They constantly set higher goals.

D They look at the worst possible scenario.

E They are driven by accomplishments, not money.

F They avoid 'comfort zones'.

What makes a successful business person?

by Murray Raphael

I have a theory on doing business. If my business is good, it's not because of the weather, the time of year or the economy. It's because of me. I'm doing something right. If my business is bad, it's not because of the weather, the time of the year or the economy. It's because of me. I'm doing something wrong. Somebody is always buying something from somebody, so how can I make them buy from me?

Successful business people, no matter what their industry, have been found to share similar traits. Today's world is no longer satisfied with simply success – we want to know how the successful get to the top. Through the years I've done some research and found there are certain qualities that describe successful business people. Here are a few:

1 _____

Successful business people are mountain climbers who, having climbed one peak, look beyond to the next highest. They are the retailers who send 1,500 mailers to their customers and yield a good turnout of 100. But instead of being satisfied with 100, they ask how they can increase that number to 150 the next time.

2 _____

To a successful person, standing still feels like going backwards. People who stay in their comfort zones do what they did before because it's 'the way we've always done it.' They run the same ads, buy the same merchandise in the same way and avoid anything new, different or unusual because they feel they might do something wrong. They blame any lack of business on the weather, the time of the year, the economy – anything except for themselves.

3 _____

Successful people follow the theory of Apple Computer's founder Steve Jobs, who said, 'The journey is the reward.' They are customer–focused, not product–focused. Their thrill is not the ringing of the register but the crowds responding to their mailing. For them, there is no greater high than a line outside the store before the doors open.

4 _____

A telephone pole had been blocking the view of Ron Bishop's Canadian gallery. He knew it would be difficult, if not impossible, to have the telephone pole moved. So he solved the problem by painting the pole with an Impressionistic theme. Once it was finished, the local paper came, took a picture and wrote a story about it. 'It was great publicity,' said Bishop. 'and then the calls were coming in for a whole week, asking, "Is it for sale?"'

5 _____

'What's the worst possible result if we follow this plan?' they ask themselves. Then, knowing that, they decide if the risk-taking is practical. However, once they make the decision, they proceed with the confidence, knowledge and expertise necessary to make it work. They understand the most harmful result and then decide if they can live with the outcome. If they can, they move ahead. Confidently. 'Every time I fail,' said Thomas Edison, 'I learn something.' He tried 1,114 times to find a filament to stay lit in a bulb. He failed 1,113 times.

6 _____

Successful people will be moving towards the pictures they create in their mind until they reach them. They can rehearse coming actions or events as they 'see' them. They are like chess players who can 'feel' the next move of their opponent and have half a dozen responses ready when their time comes to move.

How many of these six characteristics are yours?

GRAMMAR: the continuous aspect

2 Underline examples of the continuous aspect in the text on page 5.

3 Match the uses of the continuous aspect with the example sentences found in Exercise 2.

1 to talk about actions that were in progress at an earlier time

_____

2 to talk about actions that are currently in progress

_____

3 to talk about an ongoing action which began in the past and is still continuing or has just finished

_____

4 to describe future arrangements

_____

4 Rewrite the sentences using the continuous aspect.

1 He finally got through to the operator after he had tried countless times for over two hours.

_____

2 It's been several years since the research on the behaviour of students in exams began.

_____

3 I didn't stop thinking about the offer. In fact, I was up all night.

_____

4 The examinations are planned for Thursday at 10 a.m.

_____

5 The whole of this month, we have negotiations between ourselves and the Dickson Group.

_____

LISTENING

5 **1.3** Listen to people talking about success and match the statements to the speakers. Some have more than one answer and two are not mentioned.

1 Success is addictive. ____

2 Success is all about gaining power quickly. ____

3 You have to be very motivated to be successful ____

4 My idea of success is influenced by my childhood. ____

5 It's all about being the right person, in the right place, at the right time. ____

6 Educational success is not important. ____

7 Anyone can be successful, whatever their character. ____

8 Superstitious people believe success depends on luck. ____

9 Success doesn't have anything to do with business. ____

VOCABULARY: adjectives

6 **1.3** Listen again and tick the adjectives that you hear.

1	accomplished	____	10 passionate	____
2	affectionate	____	11 persuasive	____
3	allergic	____	12 photographic	____
4	ambitious	____	13 powerful	____
5	educational	____	14 psychological	____
6	electrical	____	15 skilful	____
7	famous	____	16 successful	____
8	fictional	____	17 superstitious	____
9	grammatical	____	18 toxic	____

7 Use the correct form of the words in Exercise 6 in the sentences below.

1 I would love to study _____ as I love taking pictures.

2 Do you think you can _____ the task by Thursday?

3 He kissed her _____ and then jumped into the sea.

4 It's not true at all! It's a work of _____.

5 She had an _____ reaction to nuts.

6 He believes in every _____. Even the one about walking under ladders.

7 She has no _____. She just wants to work with animals.

8 _____ is overrated. The media attention is not worth it.

9 I know the _____ but I still can't speak the language.

10 The levels of _____ suggest that the liquid would kill you.

DICTATION

1a [1.4] Listen and write what you hear.

_____

_____

_____

_____

_____

_____

_____

1b Read what you have written and answer the following questions.

1 Who is talking?

_____

2 What has he done?

_____

3 What is he not planning to do?

_____

LISTENING

2 [1.5] Listen to the second part of the interview with Richard Novak and answer the following questions.

1 What question is Richard being asked?

a) What are you planning to do over the next year?

b) What sort of job are you looking for?

c) How easy is it going to be to find a job?

2 What might some people feel about his degree?

a) It won't prepare him for a job.

b) He has done very well.

c) It's as relevant as any other degree.

3 What do we know about his sister?

a) She spent a long time looking for jobs.

b) She has done very well for herself.

c) She is doing an unsuitable job.

4 What do we know about Raul?

a) He's planning to take a year off.

b) He's going to do a postgraduate degree.

c) He needs to find a job quickly.

5 How does Richard feel?

a) He is sure that companies will be fighting to get him.

b) He believes that salaries may drop.

c) He is confident that he can do a postgraduate degree later.

GRAMMAR: the perfect aspect

3 [1.4 and 5] Listen to the whole interview. Complete the sentences with phrases from the interview.

1 _____ that, I'm not ruling it out.

2 I _____ what job I wanted to do before I chose my university subject.

3 I think companies want applicants _____ university and done well ...

4 By the end of this year she _____ for five very successful years as a Sales Manager.

5 My best mate, Raul, _____ about taking a year out until he saw the amount of money he had to pay back.

6 Personally, I think the markets _____ for years …

7 Companies _____ for people like me.

4 Match in the perfect tenses from Exercise 3 with the descriptions 1–3.

1 This looks back from a time in the past to another time before that. _____

2 This looks back from a time in the future to another time before that. _____

3 This looks back from now to a time before now. It often focuses on completed actions or situations.

_____

5 Complete the sentences with the perfect aspect. Use the infinitive or the *–ing* form.

1 _____ the report, I decided to call a meeting. (read)

2 _____ the issue with my wife, we are prepared to accept your offer. (discuss)

3 He wanted them _____ the problem by the end of the day. (solve)

4 I can tell you he's a really nice guy, _____ him three times. (meet)

5 They promised _____ the broken cables sometime this week. (fix)

6 Why has he been arrested? What is he supposed _____? (do)

READING

6 Read the four newspaper texts about the job market for graduates. Which is the odd one out? Why?

A The government is urging graduates to consider a spell working abroad, whether in internships or volunteering, to avoid the worst of the recession. Recent figures suggest there will be a 5% drop in jobs for new graduates this summer, compared to last year.

But Universities Minister David Lammy said internships can lead to a UK job. Mr Lammy told the BBC: 'If you get an internship, you are with a company acquiring skills that are attractive on a CV – and indeed, the company that you do it with might take you on.

Then beyond that, it's right to say that we live in a global market place, opportunities abroad can add to your skills and sometimes your language skills. And volunteering is always something that's attractive to employers.'

B Until university expansion in the late 1980s, only about 14% of young people entered university – which had risen to about 40% by the mid-2000s.

But the advantages of a degree have not been diluted by this, say economists.

'There has been a huge expansion of students in higher education in a relatively short period of time – but the labour market seems to be able to absorb them,' says Professor Walker.

There has been a long-running debate whether continually increasing the number of graduates will, at some point, devalue their economic advantage.

This has become a more controversial question, with students paying tuition fees and with the prospect of fees being increased.

The long-term research so far suggests that the value has been maintained – with the economy requiring more skilled workers and supporting a buoyant jobs market for graduates.

C The UK job market is continuing to deteriorate as demand falls across all sectors, recruitment firm Hays has warned. It said demand for jobs had fallen further across both the permanent and temporary sectors after a tough past three months.

The public sector is the only area to show ongoing resilience, although Hays said there were certain roles that continue to be in demand.

Internal auditors and credit controllers are among the list of 'desirables' following the credit crunch as firms seek to keep a better control on finances. Companies are also on the lookout for purchasers and IT specialists as they focus on ways to cut costs.

In the public sector, health and social care professionals are benefiting from a more secure job environment, while there is still a shortage of maths, science and language teachers in education, said Hays.

D Research by High Fliers found 52% thought the prospects for new graduates were very limited and 36% did not expect to get a graduate job this year, leading many students to continue furthering their education rather than looking for a job.

Nearly half (48%) feared they may be made redundant within a year of work.

The survey found teaching was the most popular career choice in 2009, having been the third most popular last year.

Students graduating this summer expected to owe an average of £15,700, up more than a third from the average debt of £11,600 in 2008.

The average expected starting salary for graduates was £22,300, down £400 on last year. Managing director of High Fliers Research, Martin Birchall, said the survey showed final-year students were 'gloomy and frustrated' about their employment prospects. 'Although many students began their job search earlier than usual and made an increased number of applications to employers, noticeably fewer have been successful in securing a graduate position than last year,' he said.

'Tens of thousands of finalists are now set to leave university without a job offer and feel they have little prospect of finding work in the immediate future.'

7 Match the summaries 1-4 with the extracts A–D.

1 Graduates should try leaving the country. ____

2 Still no respite for graduates' prospects. ____

3 More graduates required to support the economy. ____

4 Degrees maintain job market value. ____

8 Read the audioscript for Track 1.5 on page 88 and the newspaper texts. Tick the true statements.

1 Raul has good reason to be worried. ____

2 Richard will probably get the salary he wants. ____

3 Richard will probably have trouble finding a job. ____

4 Companies don't care about Richard's degree subject. ____

5 Richard should really become a teacher. ____

6 Richard will probably find work more easily in Poland. ____

SCENARIO: Choosing an intern

> Looking for work to earn some extra
> money this summer? Want to stay fit and
> be outside too? Our international summer
> camps for children could be the place for
> you. We are currently seeking young and
> energetic camp leaders. Interested?
>
> **Phone** 019804 324561

1 **Read the advert and answer the questions.**

1 What is the advert about?

_____

2 What sort of people would be interested?

_____

2 **You are going to listen to three interviewers discussing a job specificiation. Reorder the words to make phrases you might hear during the conversation.**

1 a pre-requisite age is let me by saying start that.

_____

2 that are fit I think essential they it's absolutely.

_____

3 some previous it would had done if they work with kids be helpful.

_____

4 probably an edge give would it them.

_____

5 have interpersonal have to they skills.

_____

6 discipline have they must.

_____

7 if they've social groups it'd be been involved in a good thing.

_____

8 campfires they can that it's essential sing round.

_____

9 be some climbing an advantage skills would.

_____

3 1.6 **Listen and check your answers.**

4 **Look at the notes made on the two candidates. Complete the statements.**

> ## Sandra Berg
> ++ Very confident
> + worked in summer
>   camps before
> - not very fit
> -- doesn't know any
>   foreign languages
>
> ## Colin Harkness
> ++ very fit
> + has lot of discipline
> - age 29
> -- not very friendly

1 One of Sandra's _____ is that she has

_____.

2 Her best _____ is her

_____.

3 What _____ most about Colin is that he has _____.

4 Colin's biggest _____ is

_____.

5 One of Sandra's biggest _____ is that

_____.

6 I _____ Sandra lacks

_____.

7 I'm _____ about Colin's

_____.

8 What _____ most about Colin is his lack _____.

A

Dear Mr Brown,

I am writing to enquire if you have any vacancies in your company. I enclose my CV for your information.
1 _____ This includes the retail sector and service industries, giving me varied skills and the ability to work with many different types of people.
2 _____
I am a conscientious person who works hard and pays attention to detail. I can work equally well on my own or as part of a team. 3 _____ I also have lots of ideas and enthusiasm. I'm keen to work for a company with a great reputation and high profile like [insert company name].
4 _____ In case you do not have any suitable openings at the moment, I would be grateful if you would keep my CV on file for any future possibilities.

Yours sincerely,

Jake Peg

B

Dear Mr Lloyd,

Please find enclosed my CV in application for the post advertised in the Guardian on 15th June.
5 _____ It involved a great deal of independent work, requiring me to make decisions myself, self-motivation and a wide range of interpersonal skills. I also attended two extra summer courses on your industry. 6 _____
I am a quick thinker on my feet, with a keen eye for detail and I would be very grateful for the opportunity to develop my career in your organisation.
7 _____ I also have the enthusiasm and determination to ensure that I make a success of it.
8 _____ I am available for interview at any time and look forward to hearing from you in the near future.

Yours sincerely,

Jake Peg

WRITING SKILLS: a covering letter

1 Complete the two covering letters A and B with the topic sentences and supporting ideas A-H.

A) Thank you for taking the time to consider this application.

B) I'm flexible, quick to pick up new skills and eager to learn from others.

C) Therefore, I feel I now have a deep understanding of what is required to work in a company such as yours.

D) I don't only have the ability to take on the responsibility of the position you are wishing to fill,

E) As you can see, I have had extensive vacation work experience in different environments.

F) I have excellent references and would be delighted to discuss any possible vacancy with you at your convenience.

G) So, I believe I could fit easily into your team.

H) My studies at university have made me ideally suited for a position in your organisation

2 Read the two letters again and answer the questions.

1 Which letter is a targeted covering letter? ____

2 Which letter is a speculative covering letter? ____

3 Where did Jake hear about the job? _____

4 When is Jake available for an interview?

_____

5 What did Jake do that probably could not be mentioned in the speculative covering letter?

3 Penny Smith wrote the following speculative covering letter. Reorganise and rewrite it to make it acceptable.

Hi there!
Are you looking for youth and energy?
Someone with lots of great ideas and full of motivation?
Do you want someone who will work the extra hours and stay loyal to the company?
Then you are reading the right covering letter! I am straight out of university with a top class degree and can't wait to start work. Just set up a time anytime for me to come in and you will get the interview experience of a lifetime. I can also supply fantastic references. Check out my website to see all the projects I've worked on.
Cheers
Penny

Tourism and conservation

2.1 WISH YOU WERE HERE?

VOCABULARY: travel collocations

1 Add the missing words to make travel collocations.

1 _____ footprint.

2 organised _____

3 _____ monument.

4 gastronomic _____

5 _____ deal

6 baking _____

7 budget _____

8 boutique _____

2 Complete the sentences using the collocations in Exercise 1.

1 We stayed in a _____ that had rooms that made you feel like you were living in a medieval castle.

2 You can always find _____ if you look on the Internet a week before you want to go.

3 I couldn't stand the weather there. Every day we had to put up with _____.

4 Some people prefer to go on _____. Then they don't have to drive around or make arrangements for themselves.

5 The menu was full of _____ that just made your mouth water.

6 Turkey has a/an _____ on just about every street corner. It's so full of history!

7 The amount of development causes so much pollution and is bound to leave a/an _____.

8 The problem with _____ is the airports they use are often quite a long way from the place you're visiting.

VOCABULARY: travel idioms

3 Read the hotel advertisement below. Put the underlined idioms in the correct place.

Want to [1] <u>lounge around by the pool</u>? Our chain of remote holiday villas along the east coast of Bulgaria allow you to [2] <u>get away from it all</u> full of noise and people trying to sell you something. With all our villas located near the National Park our holidays will give you the opportunity to [3] <u>steer clear of the tourist traps</u>. And if all that seem a bit too tiring, you can always [4] <u>get back to nature</u> that comes with every villa.

Don't delay. Give us a call today!

1 _____   3 _____

2 _____   4 _____

TRANSLATION

4 Translate the idiomatic expressions from Exercise 3 into your own language.

1 lounge around by the pool

_____

2 get away from it all

_____

3 steer clear of the tourist traps

_____

4 get back to nature

_____

NEW WORLD OF TOURISM

1 _____

1 Worldwide, visitors <u>flock</u> to locations like Gettysburg, Pearl Harbor, Iwo Jima, Myanmar, Ypres and Normandy, regions and communities that have been nearly <u>decimated</u> by war and are now benefiting from the tourist dollar.

2 This industry was increased by flight logistics, technology, and the motivation to travel abroad. Many who had fought in Europe and Asia had a desire to return to areas where they had stayed. They wanted to show their families new places and say goodbye to fallen comrades.

3 Most tourists are interested in seeing history made 'real'. Seeing the ruins of a town make the war a reality to those who were not involved in the fighting. For some veterans of war, returning to these places may provide the opportunity to reach closure on a tragic period of life.

4 There is an intense feeling one experiences at such sites. Visitors simply stand in <u>awe</u> and visit an information centre on the grounds. Tour operators rarely see a tourist who is seeking a <u>morbid</u> experience. Rather, tourists are filled with respect for the dead.

5 A small number of tour operators accompany visitors to active areas, such as those located in Israel or Afghanistan. These tours are difficult to find and the tourists are not of the same type as those who visit the historical sites.

2 _____

6 Judging by the surge since 2001 in the number of times this has appeared as a subject matter or in a session title in tourism industry conferences and programs, we can see that it is valued by tourism industry professionals as one of the most popular <u>niches</u> in the world's tourism industry. This makes sense, given recent consumer focus on healthy and organic eating and the simple fact that all travellers must eat. Not every visitor goes shopping or visits museums, but all travelers eat. For anyone who doubts, look at the increase in cooking shows featured on The Travel Channel or travel shows featured on The Food Network as examples.

7 It is not just experiences of the highest calibre – that would be gourmet tourism. This is perhaps best illustrated by the notion that it is about what is 'unique and memorable, not what is necessarily <u>pretentious</u> and exclusive'. Similarly, wine tourism, beer tourism and spa tourism are also regarded as subsets of culinary tourism.

3 _____

8 Surgeon & Safari introduced medical tourism to South Africa in 1999, offering personalised <u>rejuvination</u> packages at the Orient-Express Hotels' Africa Collection. The packages include either surgical or non-surgical procedures, with <u>recuperation</u> at the company's Westcliff Hotel in Johannesburg and Mount Nelson in Cape Town.

9 Established to provide a personalised experience for clients wanting surgery in complete privacy, Surgeon & Safari combines recuperation packages featuring <u>pampering</u> health and beauty treatments with luxury surroundings. Guests have the option of embarking on an exciting safari following their treatment as well at Orient-Express' Gametrackers camps in Botswana. Sample the elegant locations of the hotels, the Westcliff's <u>proximity</u> to local surgeons and clinics, and each property's layout and sense of privacy.

10 Surgeon & Safari works with leading plastic surgeons in private practise, and its personalized program includes liaison with a registered surgeon, on-line consultations, pre-/post surgical appointments, airport meet and greet, and special rates at either The Westcliff or Mount Nelson Hotels for the one to two-week recovery stay.

4 _____

11 **The Lake District** Not known for anything except being poor and remote when little Willie Wordsworth was sent there by his uncle. His poems turned it into an 18th century tourist destination and it hasn't looked back since. His Dove Cottage is worth visiting.

12 **Kununurra** The big movie destination of 2009, helped along by the fact this it is virtually inaccessible. After the launch of _Australia_, there are a variety of tours to the remote north of Western Australia and the stunning landscapes of Kimberley. One 1,875km route takes followers to Darwin, Kakadu National Park, Katherine Gorge, Kununurra, El Questro Wildnerness Park, Halls Creek and Broome.

13 **New Zealand** You can't actually market someone from a fantasy tale, but it didn't stop the South Island after the success of Peter Jackson's _The Lord of the Rings_ trilogy around the world. At one stage 'Welcome to Middle Earth' was plastered on the advertising boards at the airport.

1 Read the article about different types of tourism on page 12. Match headings A–I with paragraphs 1–4.

A Educational tourism   F Health/ Medical tourism

B Space tourism   G Volunteer tourism

C Battlefield tourism   H Culinary tourism

D Ecotourism   I Disaster tourism

E Celebrity tourism

READ BETTER

It is always useful when approaching a text for the first time to establish the context of the text as this will make the text easier for you to understand. To do this you should consider the following question types: Who? What? Where? Why? When? E.g.

1 Who wrote it? What is his/her relation to the subject?

2 What is the text about?

3 Where is the text related to, i.e. which place is it about or situated in?

4 Why was the text written?

5 When was it written or what time period is it talking about?

2 Match the underlined words in the text with their meaning.

1 the process of returning to feeling or looking young and strong again _____

2 having a strong and unhealthy interest in unpleasant subjects, especially death _____

3 nearness in distance or time _____

4 when a large part of something is destroyed _____

5 looking after someone very kindly _____

6 to go somewhere in large numbers because something interesting or exciting is happening there _____

7 a feeling of great respect and liking for someone or something _____

8 trying to seem more important, intelligent, or high class than you are _____

9 relating to selling goods to a particular small group of people who have similar needs, interests _____

10 the process of getting better again after an illness or injury _____

3 Read the article on page 12 again. Identify where in the text the following information can be found, giving the paragraph number(s).

1 Evidence for its success can be found in the media. _____

2 People who don't exist cannot promote something. _____

3 It's not very often that people visit to see dead bodies. _____

4 Each routine can be planned with the visitor. _____

5 Some tours take visitors to places where there is unrest or war. _____

6 A place, famous for a poet's cottage, is now a tourist destination. _____

7 People want to share a part of their life with their family. _____

GRAMMAR: articles

4 Read the following response to one of the ideas from the reading text. Add the articles *a/an/the* or zero article.

I suppose it's ¹ ____ good idea. It's certainly not ² ____ worst idea for ³ ____ holiday I have heard. ⁴ ____ need to improve ⁵ ____ way you look is something that ⁶ ____ lot of people are concerned about these days but I'm just not that type of person. After all, look at me. There's not ⁷ ____ ounce of fat on me! I must admit I've always wanted to go on safari. Funnily enough we went on one in ⁸ ____ Ukraine of all places. It was rubbish. South Africa, in fact anywhere in ⁹ ____ Southern Hemisphere sounds interesting to me for ¹⁰ ____ holiday.

DICTATION

1a [1.7] Listen and write what you hear.

_____

_____

_____

_____

_____

_____

_____

1b Read what you have written and answer the questions.

1 Who is talking? _____

2 Who is on the show? _____

3 What are they talking about? _____

READING

2 Read the excerpt from an article on volunteer tourism and answer the questions.

1 What is a gap year? _____

2 Is the future of volunteer tourism positive or negative? Supply figures to support your answer.

_____

3 What is the new development in the volunteer tourism sector?

_____

4 What is the opportunity for dishonest organisations?

_____

5 What are the drawbacks to countries having VSO volunteers?

_____

Volunteer tourism: the gap year business

In September, 2003 Prince Harry grabbed his backpack and headed off for the start of a gap year.

His travels included spells on an Australian sheep farm and community work with charities and organisations in Lesotho, southern Africa.

The path he took was a well-worn one and typical of the market at large. Post A-levels and with a career to come, he set off with the intention of helping the less fortunate.

Things do not always work out so perfectly though, and this could spell bad news for the countries that these tourists are supposed to be helping.

Recently, VSO (Voluntary Training Overseas) – perhaps the most well-known and well-respected volunteering organisation – warned many young people are wasting their time on gap years, and often spend huge sums to work on projects that do little to benefit local communities.

More worryingly, VSO also suggested unskilled Brits may do more harm than good, draining projects and communities of resources if they need training or constant help.

According to research, a staggering 10% of all the UK's outbound travel expenditure, and 1% of outbound trips, is from the gap year market. With 200,000 young people undertaking projects each year – spending an average of £4,800 – the 'voluntourism' sector is worth about £960 million annually. No surprise that those who are interested in exploiting it can take advantage of this.

But once again, the story has somehow turned around to bite the travel industry. National newspapers have been quick to twist VSO's comments, suggesting UK-based companies in the gap year market are simply profiteering.

The gap year sector in the UK is self-regulated. Of the 100-plus companies in the market, 36 are members of the Year Out Group – a non-profit umbrella organisation who ought to be promoting high standards.

Since it was set up in 1998, only one complaint has been referred to its ruling council.

Whichever way people look, the one certainty about the gap year market is that it will grow, and not just among the young.

Those in work are taking time off to volunteer, with a career break now seen as a good way to improve your CV. Meanwhile, even the retired might soon start signing up for projects in increasing numbers.

LISTENING

3 `1.8` Listen to part of a radio programme. Tick (✓) who says each statment: Judy (J), Robert (R) or Tabitha (T). Some of the statements are not used.

	J	R	T
1 Older people are better because they have more experience and know more about the world.			✓
2 People sometimes get sent to the wrong country.			
3 As people only do these once, we have to retrain new people every year.			
4 This means they can really make a difference and people will be happy to see them.			
5 The only people who win in this situation are the travel companies.			
6 Vocational Tourism is very important in developing people's social conscience.			
7 Some people think that everything they need will be found by looking at some websites.			
8 Many young women just go to the country, hoping to find something when they get there.			

GRAMMAR: modal verbs

4 Look at the article on page 14 and the audioscript for Track 1.8 on page 88 and correct the modals in the sentences.

1 This can't spell bad news.

_____

2 Unskilled Brits have to do more harm than good.

_____

3 Those who are interested in exploiting it shouldn't take advantage of this.

_____

4 Even the retired can soon start signing up.

_____

5 Young people will be better off travelling.

_____

6 They ought to put them in contact with recently returned volunteers.

_____

7 Volunteer staff shouldn't work as office staff.

_____

5 Rewrite the sentences with the modal usage in brackets.

1 I don't think the sale of the computer will happen this month. (ability)

_____

2 It's best that you don't make a last-minute deal. (advice)

_____

3 They want to change the date of the excursion until 13 June. (request)

_____

4 I think it is likely that she is lounging by the pool. (likelihood)

_____

5 It's really stupid to sit on the beach in baking temperatures. (obligation)

_____

6 If you are not careful there is a good chance that you will be ripped off. (likelihood)

_____

7 Of course an excursion off the beaten track is easy to arrange. (willingness)

_____

KEY LANGUAGE:
stating your position, clarifying

1 [1.9] **Listen to the introduction to a meeting and answer the questions.**

1 Who is talking? _____

2 Who are the participants? _____

3 Why are they meeting? _____

4 What are they hoping to achieve?

_____

2 **The following sentences will be used in the meeting. Complete them.**

1 It is an _____ priority _____ the club …

2 It simply isn't _____ for a club to survive.

3 I'd like to make our _____ very _____.

4 You've _____ very _____ about your opposition to this project …

5 What _____ do you _____ by 'have their village destroyed'?

6 The idea of a stadium near Falmer _____ just not _____.

7 I _____ where you're _____ from.

8 It's _____ for the town as a whole to have the stadium built _____ we want to stay living in a prosperous and successful city.

9 _____ I _____ you correctly, what you are saying is that if we don't build the stadium in Falmer, it will be a disaster for the city …

10 It _____ that you just _____ face up to your responsibility …

3 [1.10] **Listen to four excerpts from the meeting and check your answers to Exercise 2.**

4 **Read the comments and decide which of the speakers is most likely to say them.**

A Brighton Council   C Falmer villagers

B Conservation Society   D The football club

1 This project will revitalise the team's fortunes. ____

2 There's no doubt it'll bring great benefits to the community. ____

3 Could I just ask you, what else it will do for our community? ____

4 How does this project help the birds? ____

5 Let's think about the implications for house prices. ____

6 I'm not sure this is the right project for an area of natural beauty. ____

5 [1.10] **Listen again and check your answers.**

STUDY SKILLS: planning and organising essays

1 Complete the essay questions with words from the box.

> account for   analyse   assess   compare
> critically evaluate   define   outline

1 _____ the measures taken to curb the economic crisis in Germany to the measures taken in France.

2 _____ the sudden decrease in turtles along the Turkish coast over the last ten years.

3 _____ the steps taken by government to combat terrorism in the 21st century.

4 _____ the term 'carbon footprint' and its relevance to eco-tourism.

5 _____ the effects of the airline price wars on the tourism industry.

6 _____ the issues that have been raised whenever global emissions are discussed.

7 _____ the role of the UN in the development of Bosnia-Herzogovina.

WRITING SKILLS: problem–solution essay

2 Look at the diagram and label the notes a–h with words from the box.

> Problem(s)   Implication(s)   Situation
> Solution(s)

3 Read the paragraph from an essay based on the diagram below. Put the underlined phrases in the right place.

One problem is that there is a very beautiful medieval ruined castle right in the middle of the valley. [1] As a result it has three mosaics on the walls which are some of the best examples of their form in the world. The mosaics have made the castle a major tourist attraction and created outside interest in the region. The damming of the valley would destroy the castle and [2] on the other hand, we would lose the mosaics forever. However there are ways of dealing with this issue. [3] Moreover, the mosaics can be moved to the National Museum in the capital where they will get the treatment they deserve and, [4] for instance, more people will get the chance to see these beautiful works of art. Another solution is to rebuild the castle 10 kms away. In fact, it could even be restored to its former glory. Both of these solutions will result in tampering with history. [5] Because of this, they can also help to preserve history for longer and go a long way to saving the heritage of our country.

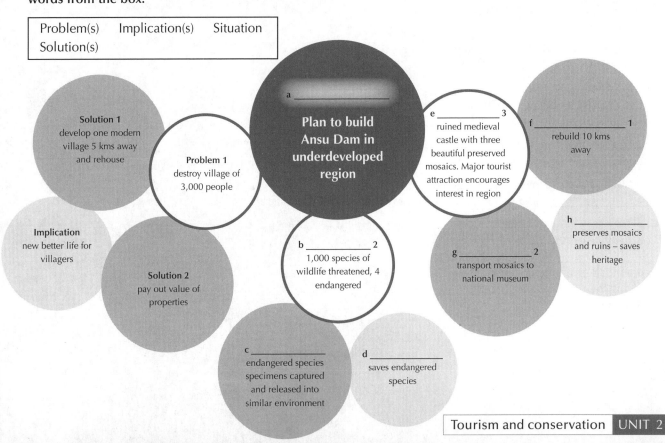

Solution 1
develop one modern village 5 kms away and rehouse

Problem 1
destroy village of 3,000 people

a _____

Plan to build Ansu Dam in underdeveloped region

e _____ 3
ruined medieval castle with three beautiful preserved mosaics. Major tourist attraction encourages interest in region

f _____ 1
rebuild 10 kms away

Implication
new better life for villagers

Solution 2
pay out value of properties

b _____ 2
1,000 species of wildlife threatened, 4 endangered

g _____ 2
transport mosaics to national museum

h _____
preserves mosaics and ruins – saves heritage

c _____
endangered species specimens captured and released into similar environment

d _____
saves endangered species

3 International relations

3.1 NATIONAL TRAITS

VOCABULARY: dependent prepositions

1 Complete the sentences with one word from box A and one word from box B. You can use the words in box B more than once.

A	B
ability	at
fascination	with
great	to
love	of
passion	for
proud	
obsession	
reluctance	

1 I don't know what Sarah will do now George is gone. He was the _____ her life.

2 The Peace Organisation is very _____ their accomplishments in the last two years.

3 Local police forces do not have the _____ arrest people in other countries and must apply for extradition.

4 He has such a(n) _____ going to football matches. Whatever the team, he always gets so excited.

5 Do you know why Jack is _____ playing cards? It's because it's what he does with passengers on all the flights he takes.

6 You have to deal with this _____ Dianne. It's ruining your life.

7 The British government has shown great _____ discuss the Gibraltar issue with Spain.

8 For many years, the Duke had a _____ classic sports cars and spent much of his life collecting them, studying them and writing books about them.

VOCABULARY: adjectives of character

2 Match words from the box with the antonyms 1–10. Six words are not used.

aloof   charming   confident   cultured
devious   dogmatic   emotional
hospitable   interested   meticulous
optimistic   pragmatic   protective
self-effacing   sensitive   zealous

1 friendly _____

2 unrealistic _____

3 honest _____

4 unsure _____

5 proud _____

6 careless _____

7 ignorant _____

8 unenthusiastic _____

9 unfriendly _____

10 pessimistic _____

DICTATION

1a 1.11 Listen and write what you hear.

_____

_____

_____

_____

_____

_____

_____

1b Read what you have written and answer the questions.

1 What is he/she talking about?

_____

2 What does it do?

_____

3 What can't it do?

_____

READING

2 Read the article and correct the notes by changing no more than four words.

1 One aim of the conference is to improve relations between police forces all over the world.

_____

2 Egyptian police have worked with Interpol to ensure convictions for drug trafficking.

_____

3 The Nairobi office of Interpol will have increased importance in chasing and arresting pirates.

_____

INTERPOL African police conference to boost region's operational capability against transnational crime

CAIRO, Egypt, July 8, 2009/African Press Organization (APO)/ – INTERPOL's 20th African Regional Conference opened today with a call for its member countries from Africa to boost security and the effectiveness of police action across the continent and beyond through regional police co-operation and international strategic partnerships.

The three-day meeting, gathering over 160 law enforcement officials from almost 40 countries and eight international organizations, will focus on bolstering police capacity, both nationally and regionally, by enhancing the investigative capacity of police and their resources to improve cross-border operations.

Drug trafficking, maritime piracy and counterfeit medicines will top the agenda.

Outlining collaborative initiatives undertaken to meet Africa's police challenges, INTERPOL President Khoo Boon Hui said that the conference would review the priorities for Africa and how best to further strengthen operational capabilities for policing in the region and beyond.

'INTERPOL understands that Africa faces complex law enforcement problems that one organisation alone cannot solve. A multi-faceted approach that pools resources and forges strategic partnerships with other international organizations is key to bringing about change and deliver better services to INTERPOL member countries, which will benefit the African region,' Mr Khoo said.

In one such strategic partnership, INTERPOL's work with the World Health Organisation under the framework of the International Medical Products Anti-Counterfeiting Task Force (IMPACT), saw Egyptian police earlier this year carry out raids targeting counterfeit medical products which netted five key suspects and the recovery of millions of potentially dangerous counterfeit medicines worth hundreds of millions of dollars.

Egyptian First Assistant Minister of the Interior Adly Fayed said that cooperation was 'a necessary requirement' in ensuring security. 'The conference is important in updating and developing joint working programmes and activities for police to fight crime and track criminals,' the Assistant Minister said.

Lauding Africa as 'a model' for international police engagement and collaboration, INTERPOL Secretary General Ronald K. Noble said law enforcement's continued effectiveness depended on the capacity of police in the region to share information and resources and to coordinate investigations via INTERPOL's global resources and network of 187 member countries.

'It is therefore essential to continue expanding beyond INTERPOL's National Central Bureaus in Africa the use of the vital tools and services that INTERPOL provides its member countries to support national and regional policing efforts so that international law enforcement can better position itself to respond to existing and emerging threats by addressing the operational needs of police on the ground,' Mr Noble said.

'A sound regional crime strategy requires further investing in INTERPOL's national and regional bureaus, for without their expertise, dedication and reach, no anti-crime plan can be truly operational and effective,' the INTERPOL chief added.

In this respect, the INTERPOL Regional Bureau in Nairobi is to play a key role in co-coordinating regional action against maritime piracy in the Horn of Africa to better support national and international investigations and operations.

GRAMMAR: subordinate clauses

3 Read the text on page 19 again. Who said what?

1 'Interpol is important to Africa because the continent faces complex issues related to crime and law.' _____

2 'Interpol bureaus, which need more investment, are key to operations across the continent.'
_____

3 'The conference is important so that we can keep up to date and improve programmes together.'
_____

4 'Before we can really respond to future challenges, we must continue to expand INTERPOL offices.'
_____

5 'Unless we can become partners we may not be able to effect change.' _____

4 Look again at the sentences in Exercise 3. Match them with the uses of subordinate clauses in the box below.

```
cause / reason    condition    purpose
non-defining relative    adverbial
```

1 _____

2 _____

3 _____

4 _____

5 _____

5 Complete the sentences with the correct subordinate conjunctions.

1 _____ that the infrastructure is in place, I think we can support Istanbul's Olympic bid.

2 The border police was formed _____ cut down on illegal immigration.

3 The Wollongong Times reported _____ things had come to a head in the tribal negotiations.

4 _____ the results are published, we'll be able to move forward with the implementation.

5 The ambassador cannot be seen to be the one _____ supplied the information.

6 There wasn't enough time to test the prototype _____ we postponed production.

7 _____ cross border smuggling of tusks and animal skin has not been stopped, the danger of elephants becoming extinct becomes very real.

LISTENING

6 **1.12** Listen to a discussion between a Foreign Minister and an advisor about Interpol's Most Wanted. Complete the sentences with subordinate clauses.

1 People shouldn't be surprised that Shin Ju Zhi is on the list unless _____.

2 It was the Chinese government that _____.

3 The Danish Government has kept the Internet crime quiet so _____.

4 Lagerman's is suspected of being involved in the Smuggler Island case but _____.

5 You could see the artefacts in Butler's house while _____.

6 Greg thought that Isaac Butler _____.

7 It is not the purpose of Interpol or the Most Wanted to _____.

READING

1 Read the description. Underline the correct words to complete the statements.

A diplomatic mission is a group of people from one state or an international inter-governmental organisation (such as the United Nations) which is present in another state in order to represent the first state/organisation in the second state. In practice, a diplomatic mission usually denotes the permanent mission, namely the office of a country's diplomatic representatives in the capital city of another country.

1 A mission describes a *place / action / people*.

2 A mission exists *in the home country / in another country / in an organisation*.

3 A permanent mission is different because *it's a place / is only in the capital / is permanent*.

LISTENING

2 `1.13` Listen to excerpts from a lecture on diplomatic missions and complete the summaries with the correct words.

1 Chancery is the place where _____ but the ambassador may not _____.

2 Legations no longer exist but were used to show that neither country _____.

3 _____ are different because, although they represent different countries, they still answer to one Head of State, even if only for traditional reasons.

4 _____ is the state that people can be in when they are staying in a place that protects them from attack, capture or arrest.

GRAMMAR: modal perfect

3 `1.13` Listen to the excerpts again. Tick the modal perfects you hear and write in the verb that follows.

1 must have _____ ☐   5 shouldn't have __ ☐

2 couldn't have __ ☐   6 ought to have___ ☐

3 might have _____ ☐   7 needn't have____ ☐

4 could have _____ ☐

4 Look at the audioscript for Track 1.13 on page 89. Write the sentences that best match the uses of the modal perfect.

1 To express past necessity or criticism.

_____

2 To express certainty about something in the past.

_____

3 To say that we did something but it turned out not to be necessary, or there was no obligation.

_____

4 To express a degree of possibility in the past.

_____

5 Complete the sentences with a modal perfect and the verb in brackets.

1 They _____ (hear) the news or they wouldn't have tried taking the dog for a walk in this rain!

2 You _____ (see) his performance in Macbeth. It really was something special.

3 The Vikings _____ (discover) America first but there is no evidence.

4 You really _____ (postpone) the meeting. I would have got there on time.

5 He _____ (get) diplomatic immunity as the police have left. He's safe for now.

6 Well, he's not here. He _____ (go) to his sister's but I doubt it.

7 She really _____ (take) that job. She'll hate living abroad.

8 You really _____ (cause) so much trouble complaining about my seat. I wasn't that concerned.

9 The announcement _____ (make) yet. It would have been on the news.

10 You _____ (know) that I wanted that job. How could you have accepted it?!

READING

6 Complete the article with collocations A–E.

A overseas postings

B diplomatic immunity

C cultural awareness

D summit meetings

E international relations

A diplomatic careeer

'AN AMBASSADOR,' wrote Sir Henry Wotton, 'is an honest man sent to lie abroad for the good of the state' — a nicely ambiguous phrase in the 16th century when lie could mean reside. Now, hundreds of civil servants, men and women, reside abroad on 1_____.
The Foreign and Commonwealth Office (FCO), has 233 embassies, high commissions, consulates and missions. Before you get too excited, diplomatic service staff also work in London. As a career diplomat, however, you could expect to spend two thirds of your working life abroad protecting and promoting British interests. These days this does not mean sending a gunboat (although consulates do their best to help any British citizens in trouble) or attending high profile 2_____ that will change the world. You could work as a political officer, monitoring developments in your host country; in press and public affairs, stating Britain's case; in consular and immigration work; or as a commercial officer. More than a third of frontline staff work full time in assisting British businesses to export or invest. In London you could specialise in relations with specific countries and advise ministers and officials.
Omar Daair, who has a BSc in 3_____ and an MSc in Middle Eastern politics, is based in Khartoum where he is head of press and public affairs and second secretary, political. 'I split my time 50–50 between contacts with the Sudanese media and political work — which involves following internal developments in Sudan. I meet with government officials and members of opposition parties to monitor events at a very important time for Sudan. To do this though you have to develop 4_____, which you can only do by living and working in the country. The job is not always exciting, although we did have a politician seeking 5_____ last week. However, although it can be just like any other job, it is an experience like no other.' This is his first posting.
After joining the FCO he was placed in the European Union Department in London, working on Spain and Gibraltar. 'I did the more political bits, but also contributed to policy about shipping, aviation, animal welfare and a range of topics I had never expected.'
Omar's Khartoum posting came after 18 months' Arabic tuition in London and Cairo. Pay for graduate entrants ranges from £20,240 to £30,330.

7 Read the article again and correct the incorrect statements.

1 The job is not always very exciting.

_____

2 Not everyone gets to be an ambassador.

_____

3 Career diplomats spend over two thirds of their time in the UK.

_____

4 33 per cent / One third of staff work in the business sector.

_____

5 Omar didn't know all about Sudanese culture before he came to Sudan.

_____

6 Usually you work in one sector and one country only.

_____

KEY LANGUAGE 1: stating objectives

1 `1.14` **Listen and answer the questions.**

1 What is the situation?

_____

2 Who is talking?

_____

3 What is the situation they are referring to?

_____

4 Why is it a problem for one of the speakers?

_____

5 What is the most likely outcome?

_____

2 Complete the beginnings of the sentences from the discussion in Exercise 1.

1 Our main _____ is to …

2 One of my main _____ is to …

3 Your _____ is to …

4 We also _____ to …

5 … should be a _____ objective.

3 `1.14` **Listen again and check your answers to Exercise 2. Match them with the objectives A–E.**

A the capture of the town ____

B to make the situation more relaxed for all neighbouring countries ____

C to improve relations between the two countries ____

D arrest terrorists. ____

E to stop the danger on the island getting to the mainland. ____

KEY LANGUAGE 2: giving strong advice

4a Complete the first gap in each piece of advice with words from the box.

| recommend   advisable   ought   essential |
| advise   urge |

1 It would be _____ for you to _____

_____

2 I _____ you to _____

3 It is _____ to _____

_____

4 I think you _____ to _____

_____

_____

5 I strongly _____ that you _____

_____

_____

6 I strongly _____ you to _____

_____

_____

4b Read the audioscript for Track 1.14 on page 90 and complete the rest of the sentences.

3.5

STUDY SKILLS: active listening

1 **1.14** Listen to the conversation from Lesson 3.4 again and label who did the following things. Speaker A or Speaker B. Two are not used.

1 showed disappointment towards the other speaker ☐

2 correctly summarised what someone had said ☐

3 incorrectly summarised what someone had said ☐

4 used a sound to show assent ☐

5 responded correctly for confirmation of information ☐

6 made a sharp physical action to show anger or nervousness ☐

7 interrupted ☐

8 asked for clarification of a particular issue ☐

9 changed the subject of the conversation ☐

10 made an incorrect assumption of what someone has said ☐

2 Look back at the responses you gave for Exercise 1 and answer the questions.

1 Who was the worst listener? _____

2 Give three reasons to support your answer to 1.

a _____

b _____

c _____

WRITING SKILLS: writing a speech

3 Read a short speech given by one of the people in the conversation from Lesson 3.4 Exercise 1. Read and decide whose speech it is.

Speaker ____

4 Tick (✓) the rhetorical devices that were used in the speech and underline them in the text.

1 alliteration ☐

2 antithesis ☐

3 repetition ☐

4 metaphor ☐

5 rhetorical question ☐

6 tripling ☐

5 Write sentences using the three rhetorical devices not ticked in Exercise 3.

1 _____

2 _____

3 _____

Good evening ladies and gentlemen. After some frank discussion it is clear to us that our neighbours do not intend to stand by us in our time of need. In our war against terror we have pursued all possible avenues that would not result in the possible loss of human life but the time has now come for us to make difficult decisions. What would you have this government do? Should we put all our citizens lives in danger or should we make tough decisions when the time calls for them? I think the answers to these questions are obvious to any citizen who loves this country. If our neighbour feels unable to stand by us, then so be it. We will be men not mice in our war against terror and anyone who stands against us will do so knowing that we will not rest in defending the rights of this country. The islands' citizens have nothing to be afraid of. We will bring peace, protection and prosperity to them and to our neighbours across the sea, I say again. It is not too late to stand with us. Let us, together, defeat the terrorists.
Thank you. There will be no questions.

4

Health and care

4.1 HEALTH AND HAPPINESS

1 Match the words from the box to form collocations of medical conditions.

intake	chest	pressure	heart	surgery
virus	ageing	pains	premature	flu
blood	high salt			

1 _____   4 _____

2 _____   5 _____

3 _____   6 _____

2 Reorder the letters to complete the collocations.

1 uminem system   4 rentiamty ward

_____   _____

2 infant ltyiromta   5 natnign salon

_____   _____

3 life pancycexte

_____

3 Read the text and add the collocations from Exercises 1 and 2.

The new Natural Health Medical Centre opens the door to a healthier life for you!

We, at the Natural Health Medical Centre (NHMC), use only natural methods and natural medicines and remedies to help you overcome the rigours and pains of life. As the ¹_____ of the average human being rises, we also recognise the need to pay special attention to our older patients.

NHMC is the first all-purpose natural health centre in the country:
Twenty Doctors provide daily surgeries for people to come in and talk about any condition, anything from worries over ²_____ (chips taste just as nice on their own!) to worrying about the latest ³_____ (did you know that natural remedies have been fighting influenza for hundreds of years?) and needing to talk to someone to just know that someone is thinking of you.
The Natural Health ⁴_____ allows the prospective mother to choose any one of a number of natural methods of birth under the supervision of our experienced team of midwives. We may believe that ⁵_____ is a problem of the past but we are still concerned about the number of complications with childbirth and in the first few days after birth. For this reason we also supply a specialised team of supporting staff who will visit mothers daily for a month after birth, watching both the mother and the child.
The Natural Health Paediatric Wing also pays special attention to children in their first years, that particularly difficult time as the child's ⁶_____ strengthens and mothers no longer need to worry about

their child's daily colds and rushing to the hospital for injections.
Our new addition is the Natural Heart Wing. Is your ⁷_____ high or do you have ⁸_____ that frighten you? Do not worry. Our Natural Health Healthy Heart Team are ready to help you through this worrying time. Although we cannot provide ⁹_____, we can make sure you never have to go through that frightening experience.
Finally, the Natural Health Centre provides a wide variety of other service from massage, shiatsu and reflexology to a ¹⁰_____ that help you hide the effects of ¹¹_____.
Who said natural health was too limited? Come and visit us and see how wrong they were!

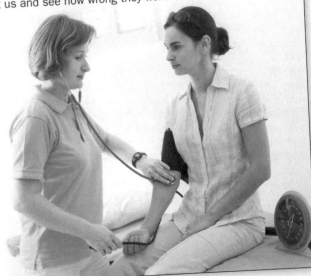

READING

1 Read the letter and answer the questions.

1 Where would you find this letter?

_____

2 What is its purpose?

_____

3 What is it supporting?

_____

Dear Sir,

In response to your article in the Post last week on XXX, I would like to suggest that your coverage was rather biased. The XXX is hugely under-rated. First of all it is all-inclusive. It doesn't just provide a service to those who can afford it <u>but</u> to everyone. This is especially important at a time when life expectancy is increasing <u>and</u> our retirement pensions have to last for longer.

Related to this is the fact that it is very cheap. All emergency services are usually covered (i.e. paid for), <u>as</u> are most operations but anything that is not fully covered is at least partially covered.

Thirdly, compared to the private sector, the XXX provides a much wider range of services to the public who are covered. Depending on the nature of your problem you will have a check-up from a GP, get treated by a doctor, a dentist or optician, receive treatment at a hospital, or a clinic, or receive advice from a pharmacist on which medication to take. If you need an operation, you will be referred to a specialist. <u>Furthermore</u>, there is even a free telephone helpline so you don't have to wait at a doctor's surgery to find out if something is wrong. Other health issues such as vaccinations, mental illness and maternity provision are included in the service. In fact it covers you for any situation and it is driven by the needs of the patients, not the need to cover costs.

Another point overlooked by its opponents is that you have a choice. <u>When</u> you see the doctor or another medical practitioner, they will be able to inform you of the care options available to you, whether they be the need to have an operation, an X-ray or scan or if palliative care is necessary. <u>After that</u>, you will be entitled to choose which kind of treatment you have.

Many people believe that the XXX does not consider alternative medicine. <u>However</u>, this is simply not true. There are several specialised services like acupuncture and hypnosis.

Finally and most importantly, the XXX is constantly controlled and under review. Independent boards such as health authorities and trusts aim to monitor the work of every medical practitioner, who are issued with regular guidelines and targets to make sure a quality service is maintained at all times.

<u>As a result</u>, we should spend less time criticising what we've got and more time thanking our lucky stars that it exists.

Yours faithfully,

Reginald G. Perrin

2 Complete the key points that the writer makes to support his argument.

1 It supplies _____ to _____.

2 Urgent services are either _____ or _____.

3 It supplies _____ than the private sector to those who have the right to use the service.

4 Every patient _____ in terms of the type of _____ they want.

5 Despite what _____, it does provide _____.

6 You can be sure of _____ at any time.

GRAMMAR: linkers

3 Complete the table with the underlined words from the text.

Notion	Linker
Addition	
Contrast	
Causal	
Temporal	

4 Add four more linkers to the table. Choose from those you studied in Lesson 4.2 in the Coursebook.

5 Complete the sentences with different linkers to those used in Exercise 3.

1 _____ you can't seem to remember things for more than 24 hours, I suggest we have an MRI scan.

2 Doctors have been working too many hours these past few months. _____, nurses are now working on average 15 hours a day.

3 I understand your concerns. _____, I can't recommend a break from work more highly.

4 _____ the X-ray machine was bought last month, it urgently needs repair.

5 _____ three years of intensive testing throughout the developed world, we are able to confirm the following fantastic results.

6 I will not be able to make you an appointment _____ the dentist comes back from his holiday.

7 Although they weren't able to reset the bone on the first attempt, they were _____ able to do it on the second.

LISTENING

6 [1.15] **Listen to a radio debate. Tick the speaker who introduces each topic.**

	Reggie	Conrad
1 Alternative medicines	☐	☐
2 Government budgets	☐	☐
3 People paying for something they don't need	☐	☐
4 Quality control	☐	☐
5 Waiting for treatment	☐	☐
6 The people who need pay more	☐	☐
7 Collective responsibility	☐	☐
8 People dying from health care	☐	☐

LISTEN BETTER

Inference: In Exercise 7 you are being asked to answer questions that may not be clearly stated in the text. Rather, you are being asked to 'infer' from the text. This means reading or understanding something even though it is not clearly stated in the text. We can use inference to understand general points, understand people's character or opinions, draw conclusions and understand meaning from context.

7 Answer the questions.

1 Where would you hear a conversation like this?

_____

2 Describe the behaviour of the two speakers.

Reggie _____

Conrad _____

3 According to the listening, tick the things that are true about either the State or Private Sector.

A The equipment is too old. ☐

B People have to wait too long for an operation. ☐

C People's taxes are higher to cover the costs. ☐

D People are not careful enough to deserve it. ☐

E If there is nothing wrong with you, there is nothing to pay for. ☐

F Service improves according to supply and demand. ☐

G Major surgery is avoided. ☐

H People who are seriously ill pay more. ☐

I There is no quality control. ☐

4 Who comes across as the most convincing? Why?

_____

_____

VOCABULARY: health care

8 **Look back at the letter on page 26 and the audioscript for Track 1.15 on page 90. Find words or phrases that mean:**

1 a doctor who may not be trained for any specific area and will meet patients on a daily basis

_____

2 a place, often in a hospital, where medical treatment is given to people who do not need to stay in the hospital _____

3 a general examination which checks your overall health _____

4 when not enough money has been provided to an institution like a hospital, by outside interests

_____

5 someone who prepares medicines, usually in a hospital or chemist _____

6 medical treatment, advice, and health education that is designed to stop disease happening rather than cure it _____

DICTATION

1a 🔲 1.16 Listen and write what you hear.

_____

_____

_____

_____

_____

_____

_____

_____

1b Read what you have written and answer the questions.

1 What is the subject?

_____

2 What is the organisation's purpose?

_____

3 What makes it special?

_____

READING

2 Read the article and match the summaries to the paragraphs A–I.

1 Being in DWB can be a dangerous job. ____

2 Frawley has a huge amount of experience with DWB in different areas and countries. ____

3 Frawley particularly remembers saving a man from the Marburg virus. ____

4 DWB has sometimes been deliberately made a target. ____

5 Frawley feels more at home working with the DWB than in America. ____

6 DWB is currently promoting its organisation. ____

7 Somalia has not been a safe place for DWB. ____

8 Frawley accepts that it might be easy to lose faith. ____

9 Frawley really is emotionally affected by her work. ____

Doctors Without Borders – medicine on the front line

A This morning, a colleague of nurse Mary Jo Frawley handed her a short *New York Times* news story about the murder of a woman in Somalia. Frawley looked so <u>exasperated</u>. 'I was just there,' she said. 'How could that be?'

B It would be easy for Frawley to be <u>disillusioned</u>. 'We were there to take care of them—to take in those women,' she says about the six months she spent working as a nurse near a string of Somali refugee camps late last year and early this year for Médecins Sans Frontières (Doctors Without Borders), the 1999 Nobel Peace Prize-winning international medical humanitarian organisation she has been active with for nearly a decade.

C It's an October afternoon in Santa Monica and Doctors Without Borders (DWB) has propped up a simulated refugee camp against the city's historic pier to show people what they do. Frawley walks confidently through a knot of tents depicting vaccination and child-nutrition stations, water-sanitation posts, latrines, and cholera-isolation areas. The people who meet her describe it as an <u>exhilarating</u> experience.

D Frawley has travelled to more than 45 countries, completing 16 missions. These missions last anywhere from a few weeks to more than a year; Frawley has spent 75 months in the field. (Only about 10 per cent of the organisation's 24,000 staffers work internationally, like Frawley; about 200 of those are American.)

E She's been in some very tight situations, that's for sure. Although violent incidents are rare, DWB aid workers have been kidnapped, held hostage and murdered. Some have even become deathly ill from infectious diseases. Some people join organisations like DWB because they find danger <u>invigorating</u>. That is certainly not why Frawley signed up.

F Frawley tells <u>inspiring</u> stories about tracking down children for measles vaccines in the remote Himalayan villages of Tajikistan, treating 400 child soldiers during their disarmament in Sierra Leone, and propping a bed up under a mango tree for a man who was suffering from the deadly and highly contagious Marburg virus in Angola. 'He wouldn't stay in the ward. He was in a lot of pain because this starts out as joint pain, then fevers and bleeding,' she says. 'So I said, "Okay, we're going to make it special for you." The team set him up under the tree with a little radio. He was <u>elated</u>. We've got a great picture of him waving. I was so <u>relieved</u> to hear he had survived.'

G At the refugee-camp exhibit, Frawley points to a large photograph of a real Somali camp and the endless rows of cardboard huts held together by flannel shirts, sarongs, blankets, newspapers and wire. She looks hard, not at the photograph, but into it. Her face crumples a little.

H It took DWB two years to get into Somalia. yet in January 2008, just after lunch, a vehicle carrying two of Frawley's colleagues in Mogadishu exploded in front of the car she was riding in. 'It was targeted. They killed us. We must have <u>antagonised</u> somebody.' Those remaining, including the fiancé of one of the victims, were evacuated hours after the explosion. 'The organization was remarkable,' she says. 'They got us out quickly. We were all in shock.'

I But she wasn't home for long. 'I needed to go back out, so I took a mission in Nigeria where I would be working with children again. We would be visiting homes and be outdoors,' she says. 'I needed to do it. It was what <u>rejuvenated</u> me.' The funny thing is, she says, is that it is not in these countries where she feels <u>disorientated</u>, it is when she returns home.

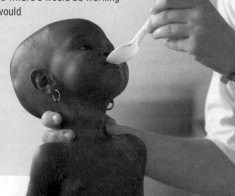

3a Put the underlined words from the text in the right column.

POSITIVE MEANING	NEGATIVE MEANING

3b Match five of the words from Exercise 3a with the definitions 1-5.

1 annoyed by something that someone has done.

_____

2 disappointed because you have lost your belief that someone is good, or that an idea is right

_____

3 confused and not understanding what is happening around you

_____

4 extremely happy and excited, especially because of something that has happened or is going to happen

_____

5 feeling happy because you are no longer worried about something

_____

LISTENING

4 1.17 Listen to the conversation and answer the questions.

1 What has happened?

_____

2 What are they planning?

_____

3 What is the purpose of the first group?

_____

4 Who does Nana's team need to meet?

_____

5 What's the advantage for the drugs companies?

_____

6 What is Penny's team responsible for?

_____

GRAMMAR:
Future forms with *to be*

5 1.17 Listen again and read the audioscript for Track 1.17 on page 90. Underline all of the phrases that use the future form with *to be*.

6 Match the phrases you underlined in Exercise 6 with the uses of future forms with *to be*. One is not used.

1 to say that something is expected to happen at a particular time _____

2 to emphasise that something will happen soon

_____

3 to say that something will probably happen

_____

4 to say that something will definitely happen

_____

5 used in a formal context to talk about decisions, obligations and requirements

7 Rewrite the sentences using future forms with *be*.

1 The old medical cards will no longer be used from 1 January.

_____

2 His scan will be performed very soon.

_____

3 Appointments cannot be made after 6 p.m.

_____

4 There's a good chance she will be able to go home next week.

_____

5 The government will definitely increase the health budget today.

_____

6 The Health Minister will make a statement at 15.30.

_____

7 She told him to stop just as he was going to take the wrong pill.

_____

1 **1.18** **Read the text on the Natural Health Centre on page 25. Listen to a board meeting and choose the correct answer a, b, or c.**

1 What is the issue being discussed?

  a) What to spend money on in the Health Centre.

  b) How to make the centre more successful.

  c) How to improve medical services.

2 Which proposal does Sarah make?

  a) Let's close the maternity ward and heart clinic.

  b) Let's cut our costs by getting rid of tanning salons.

  c) Let's expand alternative and beauty therapies.

3 Which proposal does Jill make?

  a) Let's change the name of the Health Centre.

  b) Let's cut back on the 'natural' side of the operation.

  c) Let's promote conventional medicine.

4 Which proposal does Peter make?

  a) Let's promote the maternity ward and heart clinic.

  b) Let's change our operations and create a new brand.

  c) Let's keep to the plan and just market better.

2 **1.18** **Listen again and complete the sentences.**

1 _____ promoting these services would be promoting the alternative therapy and beauty therapy side of the centre, _____ recognising where the money is.

2 I have to say _____ more than half the visitors use this part of our services _____ Sarah _____ in her opinions.

3 _____ what Sarah is suggesting, _____ forget that we are trying to be a serious health provider and all the money …

4 … that's exactly _____ that we hoped to avoid!

5 So surely _____ that using the label 'natural' is counter-productive, _____ ?

6 You _____ why I have asked Peter Jones to sit in today.

7 By this, _____ the Health Centre is not going to fail because of the word 'natural' or because you have acupuncture.

8 _____ sticking to our original plan is that this is why we started the whole project in the first place.

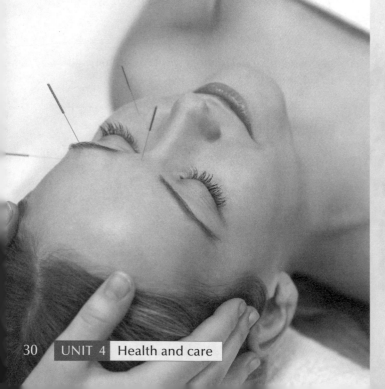

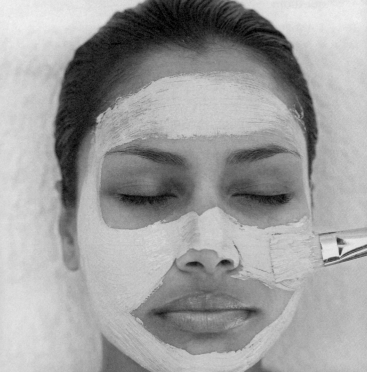

analysing visual information

1 Look at the graph below and answer the questions.

1 What is the subject?

_____

2 Where do you think the information has been taken from?

_____

3 According to the information, who has done most to deal with the issue?

_____

Stress management practices in the month preceding the survey by gender, Hong Kong SAR, 2003/04

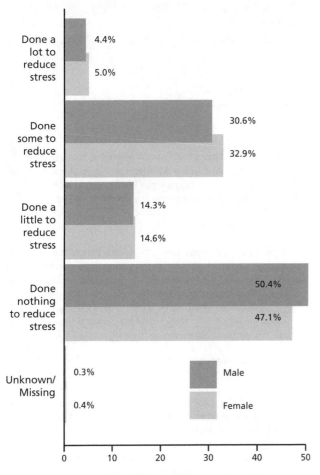

Source: Population Health Survey 2003/04. Department of Health.
Common methods used to cope with stress by gender, Hong Kong SAR, 2006
Source: Behavioural Risk Factor Survey, April 2006. Department of Health.

describing visual information

2 Summarise the information in the graph and write a clear description, using no more than 100 words. Remember to go through the following steps:

1 Read the title/heading of the graph.

2 Look at the words/figures on the vertical and horizontal axes of the graph.

3 Look at any other written information on the graph.

4 Plan your answer. Decide what the main points are and make notes on them, including key data.

5 Write your answer (main points, plus supporting data). Use linking words.

6 Count how many words you have used to make sure it is right.

7 Check for mistakes, e.g. grammar, spelling, punctuation.

_____

_____

_____

_____

_____

_____

_____

_____

_____

_____

_____

_____

_____

_____

_____

_____

5 Fashions and consumerism

5.1 GLOBAL CONSUMERISM

**VOCABULARY:
consumer collocations**

1 Underline the words that cannot be collocated with consumer.

> group   boom   spending   materialism
> products   demand   advice   supply
> society   mall   goods   phenomenon
> era   confidence   trends   issues
> choice   breed   price index

2 Complete the sentences with words from Exercise 1. Some may have more than one answer.

1 For many years consumer _____ was high – people believed in consumerism and so spent their money.

2 My _____ to you all is don't get too complacent.

3 Consumer _____ will replace consumer needs.

4 So, when the glorious consumer _____ bubble burst and came to an end, the market collapsed.

5 That's what we have consumer _____ for, after all; to help the consumer.

6 Consumerism encourages _____ which benefits the economy.

7 Consumer _____ means we can buy what we want, not buy what we have to.

8 Recent _____ suggest that we are coming out of the present economic crisis.

9 It seems that it only helps to create consumer _____ where the consumer makes all the choices.

10 _____ are made and thrown away.

11 Unfortunately it means that hundreds of thousands of consumer _____ are made.

3 Use the sentences 1–11 from Exercise 2 in the correct places A–K to complete the text.

http://www.axelsanti-moneyblog.com

Axel's Anti-Money Blog

How good is consumerism for you?

A ____

Surely it's a good thing that we can select the product we want to buy. Well, you would think so wouldn't you? However, all human beings are not the same and want different things. This means that the market is varied. B ____. Yet who wants them? Nobody. C ____ Therefore precious resources are lost. D ____.

I am not even sure about this. How does it benefit the economy? Call me ignorant but cash flow moving around is still just money moving fast. How is that good for little old me? What does more money flying about really do? E ____. Then what we are faced with is a very dangerous situation indeed. F ____. New super televisions will be made, rather than new medicine to save people.

Everybody loves shopping. If only this was true. G ____ They bought what they wanted and believed that consumerism would live forever. It was, after all, the natural way. What people forgot is that economics is not a natural phenomenon. It is created by humans. Without money, the world would still exist. H ____ Consumers fled the shops and the superstores and started selling instead of buying. Of course, then, there was nobody left who wanted to buy. I ____. However, we have learnt some hard lessons about consumerism.

As we can see, consumerism can be a dangerous thing. J ____. Consumerism is a lot less than people make it out to be. Yes, in a world ruled by money the rights of the consumer have to be considered. K ____. However, the consumer is NOT king because let's be honest, humans are not very good at regulating themselves.

LISTENING

1 **1.19** **Listen to the news item. Correct the incorrect sentences.**

1 New York is the new fashion capital.

_____

2 The survey makes its decision based on counting the occurrences of words and phrases across the media world.

_____

3 The previous fashion capital was number one for ten years.

_____

4 The economic crisis has had some effect on the fashion industry.

_____

5 Fewer people are attending fashion shows.

_____

6 The reason for the city's success is that it has more fashion shows.

_____

READING

2 **Skim the text and choose the best title.**

1 Grandfather to daughter make Prada fashion's number one!

2 Why Prada makes Milan the fashion capital of the world

3 Prada: from suitcases to catwalk. From Milan to the world

4 Prada: How a mime-artist tricked the fashion world

A What does the name Prada signify? Style and luxury, a world of designer handbags and fabulous shoes. Established nearly a century ago, the House of Prada is recognised around the world for its simple and eye-catching creations.

B Mario Prada started the Prada label in 1913. He designed and sold luggage, handbags, and shoes in two boutiques in Milan, and had clients across Europe and the US. When the big-name Prada suitcase, made from heavy walrus skin, proved unsuitable for air travel, Prada concentrated on designing exquisite leather accessories and waterproof handbags. Nobody in the first half of the twentieth century believed that Prada would dominate the fashion world.

C In 1978, Mario's granddaughter, Miuccia Prada, took over the company. Miuccia was a former mime artist who had spent five years studying at Milan's Teatro Piccolo, and had a PhD in political science. Although her qualifications didn't seem appropriate, she was clearly fashion-conscious. The label was well-known as a leather goods manufacturer, but had been struggling financially for several years. It looked like it was going to continue to do so. There was competition from other fashion houses like Gucci but Miuccia turned the business around and steered the House of Prada towards the world of haute couture.

D Miuccia had been making jet-black waterproof backpacks since 1970, out of a nylon fabric called 'Pocone'. She unveiled the classic Prada handbag which was simple, sleek, black nylon, and in 1985 it became an overnight sensation. The bag was functional and sturdy, practical and fashionable. The high price tag that accompanied the handbags was bound to cause an onslaught of designer knock-offs. This only helped to make the genuine Prada articles more in demand.

E In 1989, Prada hit the catwalks with its ready-to-wear collection of elegant, simple clothing. The fashion world took notice, and Prada's popularity soared. By the beginning of the 1990s, it was clear that Prada was going to be the leading force in fashion. Luxurious fabrics and simple styles, mostly in basic colours such as black, brown, grey and cream became the signature Prada look: sexy and confident without revealing too much.

F Now the company was established in the highbrow fashion world. Many felt that this is where Miuccia's interest would remain if Prada were to continue its meteoric rise. However, In 1992, Miuccia created the more affordable Miu Miu line, aimed at younger buyers, followed by, the Prada Sport label, a line of menswear and a lingerie collection.

In 1993, Prada received the Council of Fashion Designers of America award for accessories.

G Although the Prada look has developed over the years, and Miuccia is credited with many innovations in fabric and design, the quality of the finished product has never been compromised.

H Prada has boutiques in dozens of cities all across the globe. The shoes have become a must-have item for fashion enthusiasts and celebrities alike, and owning one of their fabulous handbags, with the distinct silver Prada triangle, is a status symbol for women all over Europe and North America.

I Prada's wide range of goods and designs continued to sell well and did not suffer during the economic crisis of 2008-09. The ongoing success of the business was proof enough that Miuccia Prada had taken her grandfather's struggling leather goods business and created a real fashion empire.

3 Read the text on page 33 again and match the summaries 1-9 with the paragraphs A-I.

1 Miuccia did not seem to have the experience but soon showed that she knew about fashion. ___

2 Prada has gown internationally and its logo has become an icon. ___

3 Prada decided to create a less expensive range to attract new customers. ___

4 Miuccia's success has made Prada well-protected for changes in the economy. ___

5 Everyone knows the name 'Prada' and what it means. ___

6 Prada specialised in suitcases and travel accessories. ___

7 Her new product was developed from a product she created before she joined Prada. ___

8 Prada soon developed a sophisticated style which became recognised as unique. ___

9 Although Prada has tried many new things, quality has always been key. ___

VOCABULARY: adjectives

4 Read the audioscript for Track 1.19 on page 91 and the text on page 33. Find examples of compound adjectives and write them in the table.

	compound adjectives
1 noun + adjective	
2 noun + -ing participle	
3 noun + -ed participle	
4 adjective + noun	

GRAMMAR: future in the past

5 Match the examples of the future past A–D with the uses 1–4.

A It looked like it was going to continue to do so.

B Many felt that this is where Miuccia's interest would remain if Prada were to continue its meteoric rise.

C Nobody in the first half of the twentieth century believed that Prada would dominate the fashion world.

D The high price tag that accompanied the handbags was bound to cause an onslaught of designer knock-offs.

1 to express the future with nouns and adjectives ___

2 in formal contexts to talk about decisions, obligations and requirements ___

3 when the future action happened, did not happen or to make an excuse ___

4 when the action definitely happened ___

6 Complete the sentences with the correct future in the past. Only use *was/were going to* when there is no other choice.

1 We _____ get the dresses ready for 5 p.m. but we missed the deadline. That got me the sack!

2 Where _____ the photo shoot _____ take place? I thought it was at the fountain.

3 Really, I _____ check the window dressing but I didn't have time.

4 Did you know that Raybans _____ become the fashion accessory it is recognised as today?

5 Madeleine _____ receive her award last Friday. Then she was off to Brazil.

6 The bottom _____ fall out of the market. It couldn't stay at the levels it was at.

7 I believe you _____ pick up the models from the Sheraton.

8 Over the next ten years between 1984 and 1994, the fashion industry _____ find that more products were being copied and sold more cheaply than the originals.

DICTATION

1 `1.20` Listen and write what you hear.

_____

_____

_____

_____

_____

_____

VOCABULARY: suffixes (nouns 1)

2 Identify examples of the uses of *-ness* and *-ion* in Exercise 1.

_____

_____

3 Complete the table.

NOUN	VERB	ADJECTIVE	ADVERB
	obsess		
		active	
	—	conscious	
	—		conveniently
	—	popular	
	sustain		
	violate		—
	—		happily
	—	confident	
	tend	—	—
	—		possibly

4 Complete the sentences with the noun forms from Exercise 3.

1 Plagiarism is a clear _____ of the copyright law.

2 They are called _____ stores because you can buy anything in them and they are usually close to your house.

3 If someone is hit hard on the head, it is important you don't let them lose _____.

4 You need to consider the _____ of the designs. Will people still want these in ten years time?

READING

A day in the life of fashion

Not everyone in the fashion industry gets to be a fashion designer. Once the designs have been made, marketed and sold, fashion shows need to be prepared, photo shoots done, models made to look good.

To get a closer look at some of the less well-known aspects of the fashion industry, *Career Monthly* went behind the scenes and interviewed some of the faceless people who work in it.

For example, fashion stylist Nelly Sykes. When asked about her typical day she replied, 'Well it won't fit everyone's perceptions. Glamour it is not! A typical day for me includes waking up at about four in the morning (sometimes earlier) to get dressed and eat breakfast. Next I have to load up my car with clothes, clothes racks and other miscellaneous stylist's equipment.

Then I have to drive to the location where I am needed, making sure that I am there at least two hours before so I will be ready for work. What this means is steaming garments, making sure all outfits, shoes and accessories are together and visible for each model to know what's theirs.'

Alicia Jackson is a couture designer and her typical day is packed with things to do, as she explained.

'Never is anything typical in the world of fashion, and more specifically, haute couture. This is what makes my work both challenging and exciting. No day is ever 'routine', although we begin and end each day more or less the same: in early, out late.

We have appointments all day. At each meeting we evaluate the progress of a project through the various stages of development. Development of couture garments requires many hours to fabricate a product that is of such superior and exquisite quality as deserves the label, haute couture. It's getting the timing right— that is the big problem.

We may begin the day with a final fitting. Here the last details are discussed and finalised with the client. A series of image sketches portraying variations of a basic design concept, accompanied by suggestions of appropriate fabrics, may be the subject of the conversation with our next client. It isn't easy to translate a verbal description of an abstract design idea into reality, and sketches help identify whether or not we have correctly understood what the client wants.

If we have been successful, we will proceed to chart the client's body measurements, which takes about twenty minutes. The measurements serve the valuable purpose of providing a numeric representation of the human form. A good fit is dependent on extensive and accurate numbers.

Before leaving, the client is advised of fabric and labour costs, and informed of the length of time needed to produce the garment (usually six to eight weeks for a suit), along with the approximate number of fittings they will be asked to commit to. Their next appointment will be to fit the mock-up, and is usually scheduled a week later to allow time to do the pattern, and cut and stitch the mock-up.'

For Alicia, time slips by unnoticed after the shop closes as work continues well into the night. The best work often is the product of late night marathons, where concentration is plentiful and focused. But sometimes, long nights result in less than desirable results and productivity is barely measurable, leaving one feeling frustrated and unproductive. It's tough to endure the long hours required to achieve the production and quality standards characteristic of couture. With haute couture, compromise is never an option.

5 Read the article on page 35. Who ...

	Nelly	Alicia
1 gets up very early?	☐	☐
2 says her work is very challenging?	☐	☐
3 spends a lot of time with customers?	☐	☐
4 spends most of the day designing?	☐	☐
5 spends a lot of time with models?	☐	☐
6 stops working very late?	☐	☐

LISTENING

6 `1.21` **Listen to three more interviews with Raymond, Helen and Luca. Answer the questions. In some cases there is more than one answer.**

1 Who will spend time thinking and drawing?

_____

2 Who has to do research? _____

3 Who spends a lot of time reading?

_____

4 Who emphasises the importance of the people they work with? _____

5 Who has to spend a lot of time at a computer?

_____

6 Who thinks their job is underestimated?

_____

7 Who will look at production? _____

7 `1.21` **Listen again and read the article on page 35 again. Match the jobs with the people.**

Nelly Sykes	Menswear designer
Alicia Jackson	Fashion designer
Raymond Heinze	Fashion stylist
Helen Mumtaz	Fashion Zine editor
Luca Canegallo	Couture designer

GRAMMAR: emphatic structures

8 Underline examples of these structures in the article on page 35.

1 inversion

_____

2 fronting

_____

3 cleft sentences

_____

4 wh- clefts

_____

9 Rewrite the sentences to make them more emphatic.

1 Fashion designers make art out of nothing.

_____

2 I had just got through the door when Vivienne rang and told me to get to Paris asap.

_____

3 I absolutely adore her latest designs.

_____

4 Modelling isn't that exciting. It's actually rather dull.

_____

5 I really need to get 100 metres of pink lace by yesterday.

_____

6 He really didn't know that the designs had already been copied.

_____

7 They took the taxi from the station.

_____

KEY LANGUAGE:
discussing hypothetical ideas

1 Complete the sentences with phrases from the box.

mean that we'd have   need to
otherwise we'd   still keep   suppose we did get
sure how feasible   surely it'd be better
that'd mean   was wondering if   we'd
we were to   we were to   would be
wouldn't

A If you get in first, there _____ a chance to surprise the fashion world.

B If _____ reserve the new show area at the Rexon Park, _____ probably get a good deal.

C We'd _____ contact the centre quickly, _____ find that fully booked, too.

D I _____ we might move to the end of May.

E And _____ some tourists coming in, _____ that be good to promote your summer range?

F I'm not _____ that would be.

G If _____ have the show at the Langer Centre, but _____ the date in June, we'd be able to get a booking.

H Admittedly, _____ you are close to the tourists at the leisure centre.

I It'd _____ to speed up our schedule

J _____ to book somewhere with a bit more glamour …

2 [1.22] **Listen to the telephone conversation and put the sentences from Exercise 1 in order. Two of the sentences are not used.**

1 ___

2 ___

3 ___

4 ___

5 ___

6 ___

7 ___

8 ___

STUDY SKILLS:
reading complex texts effectively

1 Read the title and skim the article on page 38 to answer the questions.

1 What type of text is this?

a) An analysis of the situation.

b) Putting forward a clear opinion.

c) Looking at the causes and effects of the situation.

d) Defining something.

2 What is the writer's conclusion?

a) Haute Couture is alive and well.

b) Haute Couture's fortunes will improve.

c) It is too early to say anything.

d) It seems likely that Haute Couture will eventually die.

2 Read the article on page 38 in more detail and complete the table with the key points.

HAUTE COUTURE IS DYING	
Arguments for	Arguments against

3 Read the article on page 38 again. Identify what the following refer to.

1 where (line 3) _____

2 which (line 7) _____

3 they (line 23) _____

4 its (line 28) _____

5 they (line 44) _____

6 our (line 51) _____

7 it (line 64) _____

WRITING SKILLS: summarising

WRITE BETTER

Plagiarism

When writing a summary of a text, it is important to avoid plagiarism. Plagiarism is the copying of parts of the text without making any changes. To avoid plagiarism you can either paraphrase the key points from the text or you can also put some important things in quotation marks such as:

James said 'The institution of marriage has come under much scrutiny in recent years'.

However, you should only use this when the text is difficult to paraphrase and very rarely in a summary.

Remember, plagiarism is a crime and can get you into lots of trouble.

4 Write a summary of the article. Refer to your table of key points in Exercise 2. Use no more than 100 words.

_____

_____

_____

_____

_____

_____

_____

_____

_____

_____

_____

Is haute couture dying?

Dr Heather Allan

When Yves Saint Laurent retired, his business partner, Pierre Berge, predicted that haute couture, the most expensive and exclusive tier of fashion, where dresses are handmade and cost upwards of £10,000, would die without him. His words,
5 dismissed at the time as sour grapes, now seem prophetic.

Just 18 months after Saint Laurent's last show, the Paris couture season, which began yesterday, has dwindled from a grand week to a scant two-and-a-half days. Versace, Givenchy and Ungaro are all notable for their absence this season;
10 Balmain, Nina Ricci, Paco Rabanne and Louis Feraud have already bowed out.

Old-fashioned is perhaps the politest way to describe haute couture. Many prefer archaic.

Announcing his decision to quit, the designer Emanuel
15 Ungaro, a great couturier who trained under Cristobal Balenciaga, declared that haute couture 'no longer answers, as before, to the tastes of contemporary women'. In a society that seems to value simple comfort and uses the words 'disposable' and 'convenience' as watchwords, haute couture
20 is under constant threat. Zips are simple, disposable and convenient but are viewed with distaste by haute couture aficionados. Rather, women are expected to fiddle with buttons and lace, no matter how clumsy they are.

Another obstacle to the future of haute couture is the
25 time involved in creating these pieces of art. Each piece is handmade and takes several months to make. A number of fittings are required and no change is allowed that might speed up the process or improve its efficiency. This means that those involved in the creation of these pieces are very
30 carefully trained over many years and are real craftsmen. However, with the long hours required and the shrinking market, the future does not look good for these crafts.

In fact, the markets are dwindling so fast that there are only about, at best, 300 women in the world who buy haute couture and they are not young. Little wonder then that the
35 cost of haute couture is so high. Price tags are at least ten times that of the best designer labels.

It may be premature to declare couture dead as long as John Galliano is on the scene and undoubtedly, haute couture currently enjoys vast publicity. The current cover
40 of American Vogue shows Nicole Kidman wearing Christian Lacroix haute couture. Certainly haute couture still influences Hollywood as famous actresses still worry that the dress they wear at the
45 Oscars will be copied by someone else tomorrow. Sidney Toledano, CEO of Christian Dior, recently told Le Figaro newspaper that the purpose of the Dior couture shows,
50 which cost the company €2m (£1.3m) each season, is 'to stamp our mark on the media' — the shows are attended by 180 photographers and images are beamed around the world. He compares
55 couture week, a small event with a global profile, to the Cannes film festival.

It seems inevitable that haute couture will eventually disappear. It is so out of
60 date, so difficult to produce, too expensive and has so few admirers. However the powers that be still support haute couture and the novelty and nostalgia still keeps it alive. The end of Haute
65 Couture? Soon maybe, but not just yet.

6 Technology and change

6.1 ATTITUDES TO TECHNOLOGY

VOCABULARY: technology words

1 Complete the words or phrases to make adjectives used to describe technology.

1 state-of-_____

2 old-h_____

3 inn_____

4 rev_____

5 new-f_____

6 outd_____

7 red_____

8 cutting e_____

9 ret_____

10 obs_____

11 behind-t_____

12 outm_____

13 ground-b_____

14 pio_____

2 Complete the table with the words from Exercise 1.

Positive Meaning	Negative Meaning

EXTRA VOCABULARY: words with dependent prepositions

3 Read the text and put the underlined words with the correct dependent prepositions to make the text correct.

What is it that drives us forward in the search for new technology? How can we [1] **contribute** for our hunger for new-fangled products that may have no real positive [2] **is leading** on our lives?

Particularly over the last twenty years there has been a vast [3] **impact** in the range of new technological products available to consumers. The huge amount of choice that consumers have [4] **a rise** in too many products being created and made, and fewer and fewer actually being bought. This will lead to an enormous waste of resources and will [5] **results** to the scarcity of natural resources. Already the strain on the oil industry, which not only provides petrol but plastics too, [6] **stems** to [7] **expansion** in concerns over the end date of our resources. The need to cut back on technology and return to more basic ways of living [8] **account** from our realisation that sooner rather than later we will not be able to keep producing this level of technology.

1 _____   5 _____

2 _____   6 _____

3 _____   7 _____

4 _____   8 _____

TRANSLATION

4 Translate the adjectives from Exercise 1 into your own language. Is there any difference in meaning or usage?

1 _____   8 _____

2 _____   9 _____

3 _____   10 _____

4 _____   11 _____

5 _____   12 _____

6 _____   13 _____

7 _____   14 _____

1 Read the excerpts from an article on the ideas that will change the world and put the following sentences A-F in the correct place.

A Doing so allowed it to expand to twice its original length without breaking.

B For one thing, not listening enough to chemist Geoffrey Coates.

C Examples are pine trees and soybeans that can be manipulated into biodegradable polymers as well.

D Initially, it will need to be hooked up to a tiny computer to alert the wearer to various sensations.

E Novomer, a company he co-founded in 2004, will see its green plastics used in high-end electronics in the next couple of years.

F They are hard and rigid and fragile.

IDEAS THAT WILL CHANGE THE WORLD

Electronic Skin

As fast and small as our electronics and computers are today, there is one major drawback. [1] ____ Completely the opposite of what Stéphanie Lacour is making: bendable, stretchable circuits that will one day be used to make electronic skin and malleable computers.

In 2002, as a postdoctoral researcher at Princeton, Lacour found a way to make metal stretch by embedding it in rubbery silicone. [2] ____ The next step was building a flexible circuit. Lacour, now heading her own lab at Cambridge University, did this by consolidating all the hard microcomponents of the circuit into tiny rigid 'safe zones,' which are networked to one another by stretchable metal. The final product is a silicone patch the size of a stick of gum that bends and twists like a rubber band.

The most obvious application is for prostheses. Imagine a computerized hand that can feel heat from a stove or a person. Lacour hopes to develop the first such prosthetic glove in two to five years. [3] ____ The next step is a system that mimics the shape of neurons and relays signals directly to the brain, enabling the wearer to process tactile information in real time.

But those without prostheses will benefit from Lacour's innovation as well. She envisions T-shirts being embedded with electronics that can detect if a baby has stopped breathing and a foldable GPS-enabled map. Then there are the crazier, more fun ideas Lacour dreams up on a daily basis – things like interactive tattoos that might change from a lion to a tiger to a skull, depending upon your mood or outfit.

The Next Plastic

Plastic has changed little since its heyday in the 1960s. It's still ubiquitous, oil based, and dirt and it's been polluting the world for the last 150 years. Makes you wonder what we've been doing all these years.

[4] ____ In his lab at Cornell University, he's been reinventing plastic. Making it environmentally friendly and biodegradable– with orange peels.

The key is limonene, a citrusy-smelling chemical compound which is made from orange rinds that when oxidized and mixed with carbon dioxide and a catalyst can be turned into a solid plastic. The final product can be made into anything from Saran wrap to medical packaging to beer bottles and naturally biodegrades in just a few months. And because it can be produced using recycled CO_2 from carbon-spewing factories, simply making Coates's plastic can help the environment.

Since 1999, when Coates and his colleagues first began experimenting with limonene, they've discovered a number of other natural materials. [5] ____ And more recently, they've been experimenting with artificially creating polyhydroxybutyrate, a polypropylene-like plastic that is naturally produced by bacteria.

While Coates's natural polymers are more expensive to produce than most current plastics, he stresses that this isn't just another radical innovation that will never make it out of the lab.

[6] ____ Once production is scaled up, less-expensive mainstream consumer products such as food containers will follow soon after.

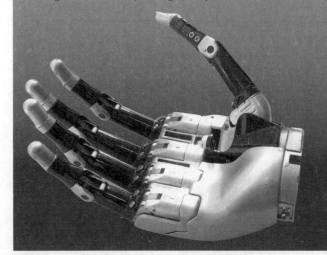

GRAMMAR: the passive

2 Underline examples of the passive in the article on page 40.

3 Write the forms you underlined in the article under their uses. Two uses are not covered in the text.

1 The agent is obvious.

_____

2 The agent is unimportant or we don't know who the agent is.

_____

3 If the subject of a sentence is long, we often make the verb passive so that the long phrase comes at the end.

_____

4 We often make a verb passive so that new information comes at the end.

_____

5 We want to avoid mentioning the agent (so as not to blame someone, or avoid responsibility).

_____

6 We want to focus on issues rather than on the people involved, especially in scientific and academic English.

_____

7 We are describing rules and procedures.

_____

4 Rewrite the sentences using the passive.

1 The court has decided to award damages of three million pounds for copyright infringement.

_____

2 They are still continuing tests on their prototype.

_____

3 When the panel told him their decision he was really disappointed.

_____

4 We will really need to discuss the implication of this development at the next meeting.

_____

5 The government are considering the idea of burying CO_2 in the sea.

_____

6 The Association for the Revival of Serious Ecological Development is funding the project.

_____

LISTENING

5a [1.23] Listen and answer the questions.

1 Who is speaking?

_____

2 Who is he talking to?

_____

3 What do the listeners have to do?

_____

5b [1.23] Listen again and tick which of the ideas the notes refer to.

	Idea 1	Idea 2	Idea 3
1 Basic everyday items can be used to make it.			
2 This improves the use of another piece of technology.			
3 On being developed, it does not need the help of humans.			
4 It is thought to be quite controversial.			
5 The idea has wider implications for other areas of research.			
6 The product can only be used on an individual basis at the moment.			

VOCABULARY: idioms with *get*

1 Complete the sentences.

1 She was sure we'd get _____ _____ but I'm afraid it was hate at first sight.

2 I wish he didn't get _____ my _____ so much. He always has the best ideas and it really is so annoying

3 No matter that there was no result after six months of testing, Dr Ryan refused to let it get _____.

4 She got _____ a flying _____ and won the race easily.

5 I never could get _____ _____ driving on the right hand side of the road, even though I lived in the US for ten years.

LISTENING

2 1.24 **Listen to the talk and answer the questions.**

1 What is the situation?

_____

2 Who is talking?

_____

3 What is her opinion?

_____

4 What does she offer to support her argument?

_____

3 1.24 **Listen again and tick the statements that, according to the speaker, are true.**

1 The topic of her talk needs to be discussed. ☐

2 She has always been concerned about if what she was doing was right. ☐

3 Ray Kurzweil should not be famous. ☐

4 The development of technology is increasing in pace. ☐

5 She did not believe robots would be able to think for themselves. ☐

6 We almost don't notice how fast things are changing. ☐

7 One day humans might not die. ☐

GRAMMAR: causatives

4 1.24 **Listen again and correct the sentences.**

A The organiser rearranged this plenary on my request.

_____

B My fears of the ethical dimensions are challenged.

_____

C Immediately I took note of the subject they started discussing.

_____

D Ray gave me an early copy of his book *The Age of Spiritual Machines,* which outlined a utopia he predicted.

_____

E With his kind permission, Ray has allowed me to reproduce the handouts in front of you.

_____

5 Match the uses to the corrected sentences from Exercise 4.

1 to say that it can be something we don't want to happen ____

2 when we allow another person to do something ____

3 as 2 but in the passive ____

4 participle to say that we didn't do something ourselves, but 'caused' another person to do it ____

5 when we force another person to do something ____

6 Complete the sentences by making causatives with the words in brackets.

1 The authorities _____ (us/wait) for more than three hours.

2 He _____ (book/publish) with Prentice Hall.

3 I _____ (not drive) without my glasses.

4 It's so unfair. I _____ (fine) for parking in a reserved area when trying to get my wife to the hospital!

5 If you ask her, Dr Summers will _____ (you/use) her laboratory.

6 The tests were a disaster. We _____ (do) them all over again by Dr Saroyan.

7 So that no one could recreate the model, we _____ (the designs/destroy).

7 Read the article and tick (✓) the following correct statements.

1 Human control will be necessary as machines will need support in doing things. ☐

2 We cannot predict the decisions that robots would take. ☐

3 The decision to transfer power to robots will be an unconscious one. ☐

4 A time may come when humans will not be able to deal with the complexity of some decisions. ☐

5 In another scenario, control will remain with most people. ☐

6 It is possible that the human population will be decimated. ☐

7 People will be given great responsibilities. ☐

8 Ambition will be removed from people's characters. ☐

9 Whatever happens, humans will be like cows or sheep. ☐

8 Match the synonyms with the underlined words in the article.

1 unimportant _____

2 predictions _____

3 destroy _____

4 control _____

5 kind _____

6 kept _____

7 good or suitable _____

8 assume _____

9 load or responsibility _____

10 majority of the population _____

MAN AND THE MACHINE

First let us underline{postulate} that the computer scientists succeed in developing intelligent machines that can do all things better than human beings can do them. In that case presumably all work will be done by vast, highly organised systems of machines and no human effort will be necessary. Either of two cases might occur. The machines might be permitted to make all of their own decisions without human oversight, or else human control over the machines might be retained.

If the machines are permitted to make all their own decisions, we can't make any conjectures as to the results, because it is impossible to guess how such machines might behave. We only point out that the fate of the human race would be at the mercy of the machines. It might be argued that the human race would never be foolish enough to hand over all the power to the machines. But we are suggesting neither that the human race would voluntarily turn power over to the machines nor that the machines would willfully seize power. What we do suggest is that the human race might easily permit itself to drift into a position of such dependence on the machines that it would have no practical choice but to accept all of the machines' decisions. As society and the problems that face it become more and more complex and machines become more and more intelligent, people will let machines make more of their decisions for them, simply because machine-made decisions will bring better results than man-made ones. Eventually a stage may be reached at which the decisions necessary to keep the system running will be so complex that human beings will be incapable of making them intelligently. At that stage the machines will be in effective control. People won't be able to just turn the machines off, because they will be so dependent on them that turning them off would amount to suicide.

On the other hand it is possible that human control over the machines may be retained. In that case the average man may have control over certain private machines of his own, such as his car or his personal computer, but control over large systems of machines will be in the hands of a tiny elite – just as it is today, but with two differences. Due to improved techniques the elite will have greater control over the masses; and because human work will no longer be necessary, the masses will be superfluous, a useless burden on the system. If the elite is ruthless they may simply decide to exterminate the mass of humanity. If they are humane they may use propaganda or other psychological or biological techniques to reduce the birth rate until the mass of humanity becomes extinct, leaving the world to the elite. Or, if the elite consists of soft-hearted liberals, they may decide to play the role of good shepherds to the rest of the human race. They will see to it that everyone's physical needs are satisfied, that all children are raised under psychologically hygienic conditions, that everyone has a wholesome hobby to keep him busy, and that anyone who may become dissatisfied undergoes 'treatment' to cure his 'problem.' Of course, life will be so purposeless that people will have to be biologically or psychologically engineered either to remove their need for the power process or make them lose their drive for power into some harmless hobby. These engineered human beings may be happy in such a society, but they will most certainly not be free. They will have been reduced to the status of domestic animals.

KEY LANGUAGE: using persuasive language and giving examples

1 Read the following short description and decide which picture goes with the description.

1 ___

The Public Invests is a TV series where inventors and potential businessmen and women attempt to convince a panel from the audience and the viewers at home to invest their own money in their ideas. The participants are given a short amount of time to present their idea or product and try and convince the panel and viewers that the idea is both attractive and financially sound and that it is a good investment. Very few people actually succeed in getting anyone to part with their money.

2 Correct the sentences.

A I say the facts write themselves, don't they?

_____

B The first figure is over one million, yes, one million.

_____

C It's wonderful that this little thing can do.

_____

D I'm not sure you know that Teleblok is a very versatile piece of equipment.

_____

E Get me to start to give you an amazing statistic.

_____

F I'd just give you a more clear example.

_____

3a `1.25` **Listen to the presentation and put the sentences from Exercise 2 in order.**

1 ___   4 ___

2 ___   5 ___

3 ___   6 ___

3b `1.25` **Listen again and answer the questions.**

1 What is the product?

_____

2 What does it do?

_____

3 Why is it needed?

_____

4 What is the concern of the members of the panel?

_____

5 What are Maria's two responses to the concern?

_____

6 Where does everyone agree improvement is needed?

_____

7 Do you think anyone will invest? What is the main reason?

_____

Are you exhausted with innumerable calls disturbing your daily life?

Do you want intruders to leave you in isolation?

Do you want to have to deal with every single call you receive?

Would your life be easier if all of this was remedied for you?

Teleblok is the best answer for someone like you! Teleblok is a little machine that goes inside your phone and through a process of answering your calls, identifying the caller, asking for permission from the caller and, if the caller is not <u>verified</u> or rejected, the caller is blocked. Teleblok will remove from your life all those telephone calls that <u>consume</u> your time and <u>liberate</u> you from spending all your time by the phone.

Teleblok will block up to 50 calls. Teleblok might save you money and could save you time.

Here is what one person said:

'Before Teleblok, I was dealing with 20 annoying calls a days. Now I don't have any at all. Except from my mother-in-law and my ex-husband, that is.'

Teleblok costs €79 only, with a 3-year guarantee. It is less expensive in the short-term than the service other telephone companies provide.

If you have the <u>inclination</u> to try Teleblok for free, please be so kind as to phone 01908 675453 or visit www.teleblok.com

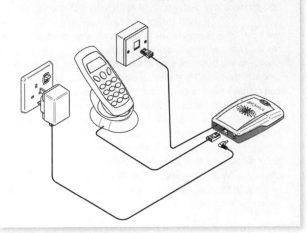

WRITING SKILLS: writing a sales leaflet

1 The owner of Teleblok employed a marketing company to prepare a sales leaflet for the product. It contained a lot of incorrect information. Look at the leaflet on the left and the audioscript for Track 1.25 on page 92 and identify the mistakes about Teleblok.

	MISTAKE	CORRECTION
1		
2		
3		
4		
5		

STUDY SKILLS: advanced dictionary skills

2 Complete the chart with the underlined words in the text. Remember to look for a word to replace the words in the text.

noun	verb	adjective	adverb	replace with
	verify			approve

3 As well as having mistakes, the leaflet is poorly written and organised. Rewrite the leaflet including the following features:

- exploit the reader's desire

- have a strong impact

- have examples of persuasive language

- keep the sentences short and punchy.

7 People and ideas

7.1 CREATIVITY

VOCABULARY: idioms with *hand*

1 Reorder the words and add *hand* or *hands* to create idioms.

a) someone's on time _____

b) full got someone's _____

c) in _____

d) anything turn someone's to _____

e) of a safe pair _____

f) on _____

2 Match the idioms in Exercise 1 with their meanings or synonyms.

1 able to do different things ____

2 have spare time ____

3 together ____

4 has too much to do ____

5 available ____

6 reliable ____

READING

3 Complete the article with the words from the box.

| unrealistic | insular | romantic | arrogant |
| emotional | sensitive | selfish | |

4 Read the article again and tick (✓) the true statements.

1 Artists are arrogant. ☐

2 You can develop creativity. ☐

3 Creative people and artists are very similar. ☐

4 Creative people also need to be logical and clear headed. ☐

5 Some of the best creative ideas are the product of several people. ☐

6 It is easy to see the difference between creative people and other people. ☐

7 To be creative you need to live on your own. ☐

ART AND CREATIVITY – Birds of a different colour

How can you spot a creative person in the street? Well it might not be as easy as it looks. Let's start by looking at some of the myths about creative people.

Creative people were traditionally seen as ¹ _____ because creative people, especially artists seemed to behave as if they were better than people around them. Artists thought because they could see the beauty of the world they knew better than the man or woman that lived in the hard real world. However, creativity and art are not exactly the same thing. You can be creative in coming up with a new idea to do something, for example, how to carry water from the tap to the garden in a leaky bucket. It doesn't mean you're an artist but it does mean you are special because you have used your creativity to find a solution to a problem in the real world.

Connected to the idea of thinking themselves better than us, creative people were seen as ² _____. Artists tended to think only about themselves and found it hard to care for a family. Creative people do need to have singularity of thought, which may mean they cannot think of anything else. For example, creative thinking usually means quiet time thinking alone. This may make people think that creative people are ³ _____, that is, they only live in their own little world, but this is not always the case. Fashion designers around the world and advertisers have to come up with great ideas in busy offices and often the best creative ideas come from teamwork. Another myth is that creative people are not necessarily ⁴ _____. This is another example of art and creativity being mistakenly seen as synonyms. Artists drew cornfields on a sunny day or dealt with every form of love imaginable. However, there is nothing romantic about coming up with a quick way to move 360 large crates from one country to another. Remember, creativity is about thinking of new ways and ideas, not necessarily making them more beautiful or romantic. In addition, a creative person needs clarity of thought, which means being in control of your feelings. Creative people can create monsters in their minds but also remember that they are only figments of the imagination. This destroys another myth that artists are ⁵ _____ and cannot control their feelings.

We have talked about artists living in their own world, which can result in creative people being considered ⁶ _____ and unable to see things as they really are. In fact the ability to be creative needs a clear understanding of the real world. Only then can creative solutions be found. Being pragmatic also means that you do not get upset at the slightest comment. Unlike the stereotypical artists, who were famous at finding insults in the biggest compliments, creative people are not any more ⁷ _____ than the average human being.

So, it seems we have been unfair to those creative people among us. In fact they are not like artists, they are just like you and me. In fact they ARE you and me, because in our own way, we are all creative.

DICTATION

1a `2.2` Listen and write what you hear.

_____

_____

_____

_____

1b Read what you have written and put the following things in the right order, earliest first.

Copernicus's theory ___

The beginning of the Renaissance Movement ___

Galileo ___

Development in the Middle and Far East ___

The end of the Roman Empire ___

READING

2 Read the article and tick the roles that Copernicus had during his life.

1 mathematician ☐

2 astronomer ☐

3 doctor ☐

4 scholar ☐

5 translator ☐

6 artist ☐

7 economist ☐

8 military leader ☐

9 diplomat ☐

MIKOLAJOWI KOPERNIKOWI
RODACY

Copernicus, Polish astronomer

Probably everyone knows the name **Nicolaus Copernicus** (19 February 1473 – 24 May 1543). As your textbooks will tell you, he was the first astronomer to <u>formulate</u> a theory of space in
5 which the Earth was not believed to be the centre of the universe. His book, *On the Revolutions of the Celestial Spheres*, published in 1543 just before his death, is regarded by many people as the starting point of modern astronomy and the <u>defining</u>
10 moment that began the Scientific Revolution. However, what is less well-known is that, in fact, astronomy was little more than a hobby for Copernicus. Throughout his life, he performed astronomical observations and calculations for the
15 Polish King, but only as time permitted and never in a professional capacity. The reality is that Copernicus was a very gifted man who tried his hand at a wide variety of different disciplines. To begin with, did you know that for most of
20 his life, Copernicus was a burgher, or respected citizen of the town of Frombork? This meant that he played an active role in the political and social life of the town. Not content with this role alone, from 1516–21,
25 Copernicus lived at Olsztyn Castle as an economic administrator. While he was in residence, Olsztyn was <u>besieged</u> by the Teutonic Knights during the Polish-Teutonic War (1519–1521) and Copernicus was put in charge of the defences of Olsztyn at
30 the head of the Royal Polish forces. His successful defence of the city brought him fame in Poland long before his astronomical theories did. As a sign of respect for his work on behalf of the kingdom, he represented Poland in all of the
35 <u>subsequent</u> peace negotiations. From this time on, Copernicus worked for years with the royal government, travelling extensively on government business and as a diplomat. Yet it was in the area of the economy that he next made
40 his mark. In 1526, Copernicus wrote a study on the value of money, *Monetae cudendae ratio*. In it he formulated an early version of the theory, now called 'Gresham's Law,' that 'bad' money (i.e. coins that are of a low value because they
45 are, for example, made out of tin) drives 'good' (i.e. coins that represent their value, for example, those that are made out of gold) out of <u>circulation</u>. The study came to the attention of Poland's King Sigismund I the Old and as a result he was asked
50 to participate in many discussions in government about coin <u>reform</u>. Copernicus' recommendations on monetary reform were very popular at that time. For most people, that would be more than
55 enough, but Copernicus also showed that he had considerable medical skills. Only two years before his death, we have evidence of him being urgently summoned to Königsberg to treat a counsellor, who was dangerously ill.
60 More evidence of his amazing abilities surfaced even after his death. In 1551, his *Prutenic Tables* were published. These astronomical tables were quickly <u>adopted</u> by astrologers and astronomers, in place of the more traditional tables.
65 Copernicus died on 24 May 1543. <u>Legend</u> has it that the first printed copy of *De revolutionibus* was placed in his hands on the very day that he died, allowing him to say farewell to his life's work. He is reputed to have awoken from a <u>stroke</u>-
70 induced coma, looked at his book, and then died peacefully. Copernicus was much more than an astronomer. Among his many responsibilities, astronomy was not so much a <u>vocation</u>, more a hobby — yet it
75 was in that field that he made his mark upon the world.

3 Read the article on page 47 again and decide whether the following are true (T), false (F), or not mentioned (NT).

1 His book was not published until after he died. ___

2 Astronomy was not his career. ___

3 He lived his whole life in his birthplace. ___

4 His economic theory later became famous under another name. ___

5 He successfully protected Polish cities from the Teutonic Knights. ___

6 He advised many monarchs. ___

7 New works of his were published after his death. ___

8 We know he saw his book just before he died. ___

EXTRA VOCABULARY: words from the text

4 Match the underlined words in the text on page 47 with the definitions (1–10).

1 a change or changes made to a system or organisation in order to improve it. _____

2 significant or giving meaning to something of something else. _____

3 the exchange of information, money, etc. from one person to another in a group or society _____

4 to take the place or position of something or someone _____

5 an artery in someone's brain suddenly bursts or becomes blocked, so that they may die or be unable to use some muscles _____

6 to develop something such as a plan or a set of rules, and decide all the details of how it will be done _____

7 when a city or castle is surrounded by a military force _____

8 an old, well-known story, often about brave people, adventures, or magical events _____

9 happening or coming after something else _____

10 a particular type of work that you feel is right for you _____

GRAMMAR: quantifiers

5 Complete the table with the modifiers in the box, according to their use.

many	either	every	some	no	any
(a) few	most	several	all	none	both
a lot of	much				

+ singular noun	+ uncountable noun / plural noun

6 Fill the gaps with the right quantifier.

1 I'm pretty sure _____ philosophers made the same statement. They agreed on everything else.

2 _____ single explanation of evolution has ever been good enough for me.

3 Do you have _____ idea how much trouble you have caused?

4 _____ of your formulations are correct. Do every single one of them again.

5 It really doesn't matter which of the two seminars you attend. _____ one will be interesting.

6 _____ people ever get to see Dr Engelman. He's a recluse.

READING

1 Read the article below and match the headings in the box with the paragraphs.

> Zero   Vaccination   World Wide Web
> Farming   Gravity   Consciousness
> Human rights   E=mc²

2 Read the article again. Which idea …

1 opens up a new world with a large number of choices? ____

2 was based on something observed? ____

3 was probably the earliest idea? ____

4 assumes that humans are interested in why they do things? ____

5 stems from the way people are treated during times of conflict?____

6 had existed for some time before the western world found out about it? ____

7 is a mathematical formula derived from a theory? ____

8 takes something harmful and uses it to rejuvenate or cure? ____

8 Ideas that changed the world

We have compiled a list of eight ideas mankind should be thankful for.

A _____
Ask people what the most important historical revolution is and their answers might include: the Industrial Revolution, the Information Revolution, or maybe even the French Revolution. But without the Neolithic Revolution, none of the above would have taken place. It is this period of time, more than 14,000 years ago, which modern-day farming can be traced back to.

B _____
When Freud, the father of psychoanalysis, suggested that our behaviour is not always ruled by our conscious thoughts, nor is it always in our best interests, he formed the basis of the idea that individuals can be curious about themselves and make a study of their own minds. He thought people talking in certain situations could let out ideas from the unconscious in dreams or through slips of the tongue – hence the term 'Freudian slip.'

C _____
Deduced from Einstein's theory of relativity, this formula suggests that

tiny amounts of mass can be converted into huge amounts of energy. So, next time your handy in-car navigation gadget guides you home flawlessly, remember, you have one man to thank for not getting lost.

D _____
Today, vaccines are widely available for common illnesses which were once life-threatening, as well as for more severe conditions like cervical cancer. The origin of vaccines – which involve introducing an antigen which encourages the body to produce

antibodies boosting the body's immunity to a particular disease – is thought to be 17th century India, when powdered smallpox scabs were used to inoculate people against the disease.

E _____
Although the concept has been batted around by philosophers for centuries, one of the first modern milestones was the UN's declaration, which reasserted the concept after the horrors of World War II. The movement's next landmark moment was in 1961 when British lawyer Peter Benenson wrote a newspaper appeal, 'The Forgotten Prisoners,' calling for an international campaign to fight the imprisonment of people for their political and religious beliefs. There were thousands of responses and Amnesty International was born.

F _____
In a matter of decades since it was invented in 1989 by English scientist Tim Berners-Lee, it has grown from a few pages to somewhere in the hundreds

of billions, according to best guesstimates. Amongst all those pages exist a myriad of sites giving people access to information and opportunities that didn't exist previously.

G _____
Although it's been around since the time of the Babylonians, it didn't infiltrate Western thinking until the 12th Century when Italian mathematician, Leonardo Fibonacci included it in his book _Liber Abaci_. Once it was finally adopted, it paved the way for the concept of decimals, allowing mankind to advance its knowledge of mathematics and logic.

H _____
The well-known story of the apple that fell on Sir Isaac Newton's head inspiring him to come up with his 'Universal Law' is probably apocryphal. However it happened, there is no doubt that Newton's insight was brilliant: He supposed that if this 'stuff' could reach the top of a tree to make an apple fall to the ground, perhaps it could reach into orbit and beyond to affect the orbit of the Moon.

EXTRA VOCABULARY: definitions

3 Match the underlined words or phrases from the article on page 49 with the definitions 1–7.

1 a story that is well-known but probably not true
_____

2 useful _____

3 to find the origins of when something began or where it came from _____

4 without making any mistakes _____

5 very many _____

6 to discuss various ideas or suggestions
_____

7 substances produced by your body to fight disease
_____

LISTENING

4 [2.3] Listen to some professors talking about the ideas that changed the world and answer the questions.

1 What could humans consider, once the food issue was solved? _____.

2 Where can we find examples of man's interest in the unconscious? _____

3 What did doctors fail to do, that resulted in babies dying?_____.

4 What was indirectly responsible for money?
_____.

5 What do vaccines allow people to do?

_____

GRAMMAR: conditionals

5 [2.3] Listen again and complete the sentences.

1 If farming _____ exist then neither _____ development.

2 If you _____ any book, comic or watch any film in popular culture, you _____ the unconscious.

3 If it _____ we _____ nuclear power.

4 If we _____ zero then we _____ mathematics.

5 If numbers _____ we _____ money, economics and all of that.

6 Look at the audioscript for Track 2.3 on page 92 and find examples of the following:

a) Zero conditional:

_____

b) First Conditional:

_____

c) Second Conditional:

_____

d) Third Conditional:

_____

e) Mixed Conditional:

_____

7 Match the conditionals from Exercise 6 with the usages.

1 to talk about an unlikely possibility, unreal situation or to give advice. ____

2 to talk about present or past results of unreal situations. ____

3 to talk about situations that are contrary to the facts, to express regrets and criticise others. ____

4 to talk about real possibilities, promises or warnings. ____

5 To talk about actions that happen every time a condition is fulfilled and for instructions. ____

8 Rewrite the sentences using conditionals.

1 The Senator was assassinated because he didn't listen to his wife and stay at home.

_____

2 We want to publish his theory but he has to provide the evidence.

_____

3 Those of you who cannot attend should inform us as soon as possible.

_____

4 Because I know the story is apocryphal I don't believe you.

_____

5 We would like to reconsider our decision but can't unless you can get proper funding for your project.

_____

KEY LANGUAGE:
approving ideas, expressing doubt, objections

1 Reorder the words to make key phrases.

A it might a problem such not be big

_____

B real problems see some can I

_____

C don't think feasible I just it's

_____

D a really it's a think I good suggestion

_____

E as much as cost may not you think it

_____

F work really it will?

_____

G in my project good, it's a opinion

_____

H on I'm not this one too keen

_____

I a great like it idea sounds!

_____

J a option it be very expensive could

_____

K the projects the some must be long term of

_____

2 Complete the conversations with phrases from Exercise 1. More than one answer is possible.

1 **A:** What's your opinion on the conservation project?

   B: Well, _____. However, I'm not sure it matters what I think.

2 **A:** So what do you think of the ideas for the Olympics?

   B: They all sound good but _____. It'll be a waste of money if they can't continue once the Olympics is over.

3 **A:** _____

   B: Why not, we've got all the resources and we've got the funding

4 **A:** I am concerned about the amount of money we have to spend.

   B: _____ I've already spoken to a few suppliers and they are ready to negotiate a discount.

5 **A:** It looks really good on paper but _____. I have my doubts.

   B: Well, to reassure you, here is a video of the model being tested.

6 **A:** So what do you think?

   B: It's a great presentation but _____. I don't know why. I just have a feeling. What else have you got?

STUDY SKILLS: critical thinking

1 [2.4] **Listen to a university radio programme and answer the questions.**

1 What is the topic?

_____

2 What is the speaker's opinion?

_____

3 How does she sound?

_____

4 Have they used critical thinking to express their argument? Give three reasons why/why not.

_____

_____

_____

2 [2.4] **Listen again and correct the incorrect notes.**

1 People who agree with the questions are to blame for classes being late.

_____

2 Students are always complaining /angry about work the professor assigns.

_____

3 Why spend no money when we care so little?

_____

4 We don't need to change our behaviour.

_____

5 College is all about growing up and doing extracurricular activities.

_____

6 All professors are under pressure.

_____

7 Our country can only get better.

_____

8 We should want to make a difference in the world.

_____

WRITE/SPEAK BETTER

When showing what you think, do the following:

state one point at a time – you can start by saying 'I think (main point)…'

elaborate what you mean (i.e. make it clear) – you can say 'In other words…. (elaborate)…'

give examples that connect your thoughts to life experiences – you can say 'For example …'

use analogies and metaphor to help people understand, e.g. 'Critical thinking is like an onion. It has many layers.' or 'Life is like a box of chocolates. You never know what you are going to get.' You can also say 'To give you an analogy …'

WRITING SKILLS: writing an opinion-led essay

3 **Do you agree or disagree with the points made in the radio programme from Exercise 1? Write your opinions in the table below.**

Note: A good idea when you are preparing an argumentative essay is to outline the arguments against you so you can answer them.

ARE STUDENTS LAZY?	
FOR	AGAINST

4 **Write an argument-led essay, using the points you made above.**

WRITE BETTER

It's important that when you make a point, your thinking is relevant and clear. Consider the following questions when preparing your arguments:

Am I focused on the main problem / task?

How are the parts connected?

Does my information relate directly to the problem / task?

Where do I need to focus my attention?

Am I being diverted to unrelated issues?

Is there any relevant information I am not considering?

_____

_____

_____

_____

_____

8 Journalism and media

8.1 BREAKING NEWS

1 Match the words and phrases from the box to make collocations.

chequebook	circulation	coverage
figures	journalism	laws	libel	media
ratings	viewing	wars

1 _____   4 _____

2 _____   5 _____

3 _____   6 _____

2 Rearrange the letters to make other words about the media.

1 cypravi   _____

2 tionulaceps   _____

3 heatsdroeb   _____

4 diotalb   _____

5 tibednsou   _____

6 sbia   _____

7 nisp   _____

8 leaddnie   _____

9 creous   _____

10 copos   _____

3 Use the words and phrases from Exercises 1 and 2 to complete the text.

In reality, journalism has very little to do with a story that needs to be told. It has more to do with ¹_____: how many papers you will sell, or how much ²_____ your story will get from the media. For this reason, every journalist is after the big ³_____, that story which no one else has. However, no story, or even the ⁴_____ who got you that story, will stay secret. So the next thing you need to consider is the ⁵_____ you will give to the story. When doing this you have to stay on the right side of the ⁶_____. Too many journalists have used ⁷_____ instead of fact or not properly respected someone's ⁸_____ and had their careers destroyed in court. ⁹_____ papers are generally more likely to take a risk than a ¹⁰_____ but they are all involved in ¹¹_____ with each other so are hungry for the big story.

4 Read the definitions and choose the right person.

1 someone who is employed by a newspaper or a television station, etc. to report news from a particular area or on a particular subject
a) anchor   b) columnist
c) correspondent   d) editor

2 someone whose job is to make sure that people know about a new product, film, book, etc. or what a famous person is doing
a) paparazzo   b) producer
c) publicist   d) publisher

3 someone who writes articles, especially about a particular subject, that appear regularly in a newspaper or magazine
a) reporter   b) columnist
c) producer   d) correspondent

4 the person who is in charge of a newspaper or magazine, or part of a newspaper or magazine, and decides what should be included in it
a) editor   b) anchor
c) producer   d) reporter

DICTATION

1a [2.5] Listen and write what you hear.

_____

_____

_____

_____

_____

_____

_____

1b Read what you have written and answer the questions.

1 Who is talking?

_____

2 What is she referring to?

_____

3 What was wrong with it?

_____

READING

2 Complete the article with sentences A-F.

A One of the toughest things to keep in mind is that _reporters are just people doing their jobs._

B Another bad sign is the reporter that calls and asks long detailed leading questions.

C It may sound simple, but few reporters know the subject.

D In an interview, every single thing you say to a reporter is on the record and will appear in print and online, verbatim, with your name next to it, forever.

E Most of us would never expect to meet a journalist or talk on a live show.

F Journalists cannot make you answer a question.

How to give a successful interview

1 _____ However, imagine this. You're a manufacturer of coffee cups and local radio invites you to talk about your new designs! You may want to decline but that would be a mistake because, after all, interviews can be free marketing ... if they are done properly.

Here are some tips for making an interview with the media work for you.

2 _____ A good reporter does research on the interview subjects. A great interview with a reporter feels like a natural conversation with a friend you've never met. They'll ask you questions that you haven't answered a hundred times before, and really want to explore your experiences that have led to something newsworthy. If you notice any of these qualities, relish the opportunity because these kinds of interviews account for maybe five percent of the interviews I've ever done. The biggest sign you're in a bad interview is when you can hear a keyboard involved. The interview will take twice as long as it should because you'll have to keep pausing while they type.

3 _____ Reporters that ask questions like this will basically write an entire article and then at the end, call a couple of people to fill in the blanks with quotes supporting points of view they already wrote about. The best thing to do is find out about the person who is interviewing you beforehand. Who has he or she interviewed before? Call them and find out their experiences. It's never a bad thing to be prepared. Next, remember that you don't have to answer any question you don't want to. 4 _____ They might ask how much you are earning, your family, or where you live but if you feel remotely uncomfortable answering a question, stop the reporter ASAP and say you won't answer the question. Don't say anything you wouldn't want to see plastered as the headline.

Though it's tempting to see the press as dangerous, the truth is, you'll get the most value out of the press by having good relationships with them. 5 _____ So that means they want to be good at it, please their bosses, and impress their peers. If you want to increase the chances of good coverage, of getting a quote in a story, or having your work mentioned, one of the best things to do is simply make the reporter's job easier. Recommend other good sources of information (peers, people involved in the story, people that cover the subject), and have a portfolio or background info on yourself and your work available. A standard short biography and some quick links to information about your area of expertise are a great help.

6 _____ It will often be out of the context in which you said it. You might consider scripting what you're going to say, and repeating it over and over. You can also think about going _off_ the record for information that's particularly sensitive, or for announcements that you'd like to embargo until a certain date and time. Be sure to say the exact words 'This is off the record.' clearly and out loud before you even start talking about anything that's not for publication.

Finally, unless you excel at speaking and thinking on your feet, or you have a lot of experience, it is probably a good idea to steer clear of live shows on the radio or TV. Podcasts are fine because they are edited but remember live really DOES mean live.

3 Read the article again and complete the pieces of advice.

1 _____ about the interviewer _____ the interview.

2 Don't _____ a question unless _____.

3 Only _____ that you would be happy to see _____.

4 Remember that reporters are _____ too.

5 Try and _____ the interviewer _____ for the interview.

6 Remember that _____ is ON THE RECORD.

7 _____ what you want to say before the interview can help you.

8 If you want to say something _____ say it loud.

9 Unless you are really _____, try and _____.

GRAMMAR: verb patterns

4 Look back at the article on page 54 and add one example for each verb pattern below.

1 verb + infinitive without *to*

_____

2 verb + (object) + infinitive with *to*

_____

3 verb + (object) + -*ing* form

_____

4 verb + (object) + preposition + -*ing* form

_____

5 verb + -*ing* or infinitive

_____

5 Complete the sentences using the correct verb pattern.

1 He was _____ the Orlic prize for _____ an article on famine in Africa (award / write)

2 I _____ in the telesales department because there is so much free time. (like / work)

3 Have you ever _____ as a correspondent in Mongolia? (consider / work)

4 The journalist _____ him _____ the whole story before the police arrived. (urge / tell)

5 Because the task was done so poorly, they _____ us _____ the task again. (make / do)

6 You must _____ me you _____ more carefully next time. (promise / drive)

7 I _____ the car _____ but I didn't hear it come back. (hear / leave)

LISTENING

6 [2.6] Listen to the interview and tick the statements that are correct.

1 Joanne works for a department store. ☐

2 Sunshine's is introducing a new promotion. ☐

3 Sunshine's has very different types of customers. ☐

4 There is a difference in quality between the different types of beans. ☐

5 Joanne agrees with John about the quality of the beans. ☐

6 The interview will be edited. ☐

7 John doesn't want to talk to Joanne. ☐

8 Joanne isn't very good at answering questions. ☐

7a [2.6] Listen again and give reasons why this was a bad interview.

1 _____

2 _____

3 _____

4 _____

5 _____

6 _____

7 _____

7b Look back at the article on page 54 and check your answers.

1a 2.7 Listen to the conversation between an employee and a member of Human Resources and write the questions the employee asks.

	Y	N	D
1 _____			
2 _____			
3 _____			
4 _____			
5 _____			
6 _____			

1b Choose the correct answers to the questions. Tick Y (Yes), N (No), or D (Depends).

VOCABULARY: idioms with *keep*

2 2.7 Listen again and make a list of the idioms with *keep* that are used.

_____

3 Complete the idioms with *keep* in the following sentences.

1 He's a tough interviewer but if you keep _____ you'll be fine.

2 Someone is definitely hacking into the system. Can you keep _____ the staff in your department?

3 I'm not very confident that the proposal will get through but keep _____ and who knows what will happen.

4 It's easy to become subjective in situations like this. That's why it's important to keep _____.

5 Ever since he made a fool of himself on the talk show he's been trying to keep _____.

TRANSLATION

4 Translate the idioms in Exercise 3 into your own language so that the meaning stays the same.

1 _____   4 _____

2 _____   5 _____

3 _____

READING

5 Read the email on page 57 and answer the questions.

1 What's the topic of the email?

_____

2 Why would this be useful to the IT department?

_____

3 What do the reports recommend?

_____

4 Why is the text reliable?

_____

5 What benefit is there for marketing departments?

_____

6 Look at the underlined phrases/sentences in the email on page 57 and decide which of the following sentences has the same meaning.

1 a) Both agree that banning employees from using social networking sites is a good idea.

b) Both feel that productivity can be increased by banning some employees from using the sites.

c) Both say that banning all employees is not useful as it does not increase productivity.

2 a) Companies should understand that social networking is part of social life and consider it in their policies at a variety of levels.

b) Companies should have policies for dealing with social networking that recognise social networking as part of the working experience.

c) Companies should incorporate social networking into the social life of the company.

3 a) IT departments understand the advantages of using social networking sites.

b) IT departments can't seem to understand how useful using social networking sites could be.

c) No one is telling IT departments how useful social networking sites can be.

4 a) Our competitors think we are not being fair but they need to understand how the business world has changed.

b) Our competitors think that we cannot do our job properly but they don't understand the new business world.

c) Our competitors need to understand how the business world has changed and then they can accuse us.

From: Marketing
To: IT
Subject: Thought you should see this ...

Both Gartner, the world's leading information technology research and advisory company, and Huddle.net have found that banning the use of social networking sites in the workplace could be doing more harm than good.

The argument that heads of department should deal with their staff more effectively and not limit their Internet access has been reignited with news that it's not always such a great idea to ban community applications in the workplace.

1 Both Gartner and business social networking developer Huddle have brought out reports stressing the demerits of blanket bans on employees using the sites as a means to spur productivity.

Gartner's report concludes that organisations should think again about stopping the workforce from using social applications.

2 Organisations should anticipate web participation 'as part of the social experience and come up with a multilevel approach to policies for effective governance', according to Gartner.

Huddle claims to have uncovered the true extent of social network censorship in the UK with its latest report, for which they questioned 202 local authority officials on the subject of 'social collaboration in the public sector'.

The survey found that up to 56 percent of workers in the public sector are banned from using social networking sites such as Facebook, despite more than a third of those asked wishing to use them at work.

A further 38 percent of respondents think that the government as a whole should operate a social network across all departments.

'IT departments hear 'Facebook' and clam up.

3 'The message that social networking sites can be used to the advantage of companies is not getting through to them'.

This is, of course not news, to the more forward-thinking of companies who are using social networking sites very effectively. These companies have found these sites extremely useful in making contacts across the market, exchanging information and developing clients. 'You only need to take a quick look into a web environment like Second Life and see all the business generated there' says Marketing Manager of the Idle Group, Ash Dhoji.

4 We have been accused of unprofessionalism and even under-handedness by our competitors but they need to take a good look at the new business world he said.

Alastair Mitchell, chief executive of Huddle, endorsed this view. 'There's more to social networking than just consumer sites.

5 Public sector workers already know that efficiencies can be made by technologies that encourage collaboration for work purposes., so it's time that IT heads look around and smell the coffee'.

---

5 a) Effectiveness in the public sector is heavily reliant on getting outside help

b) People in the public sector know that working together makes work more effective

c) Collaboration is recognised as important in making work more public.

GRAMMAR: prepositional verbs

7 Underline the multi-word verbs in the email that match 1–9 below.

1 to take necessary action to solve a problem

2 published

3 consider

4 think of an idea, answer

5 stop talking

6 to succeed in communicating a message

7 investigate

8 to say someone is guilty of something

9 observe carefully

8 Complete the sentences with the prepositional verbs from the box.

accuse of	clam up	come across
come up with	deal with	look into
get over	get through	

1 He never really _____ the claims they made about his business in the press.

2 You won't _____ to him on the subject of controlling his finances. Just mention money and he _____ completely.

3 I'm concerned about the budget projections. Could you _____ it in more detail?

4 I'm very disappointed with your proposals. You'd better _____ a better one pretty quick.

5 Have you _____ any mention of the Spenser archives in your research?

6 Who needs to be _____ to get the project accepted?

7 I don't think you should _____ anyone _____ anything. You're not exactly innocent yourself.

KEY LANGUAGE: being cautious

1 Match the first half of the sentences A–H with the second half 1–8.

A It's just speculation

B We need to

C If that is the case,

D If you don't get your facts straight in the presentation,

E It could land us

F If we get our sales message wrong

G We need to hold fire

H It is

1 he could give us a really hard time in the question session.

2 in court.

3 a very sensitive issue.

4 think this one through again.

5 on our part.

6 on this.

7 it'll have a bad effect on the whole promotion campaign.

8 we could be in hot water.

2 Complete the dialogue with sentences from Exercise 1.

TANYA: This is a very serious decision ¹___.

ROB: But we haven't got time! A decision needs to be made now!

TANYA: I'm all prepared for the presentation to Mike.

ROB: I hope so, ²___ afterwards.

TANYA: I am afraid we are beginning to suspect there were mistakes in the article we published.

ROB: I hope that's not true! ³___ being charged with libel!

TANYA: We need to tread carefully. ⁴___ and I don't want to upset anyone.

ROB: Don't worry, Tanya, I've put my best people on it.

TANYA: Initial research suggests that people like the advert.

ROB: Well, get some more customers to listen to it. ⁵___.

TANYA: Are we all agreed on the action?

ROB: Well I'm not sure. We are acting on something we are not sure of. ⁶___ that things will improve.

TANYA: ⁷___

ROB: OK. Let's give it a week and see what the reaction is and then decide what to do.

TANYA: He's decided to refuse our offer and is speaking to a solicitor.

ROB: ⁸___ We'd better call a meeting to decide what to do.

STUDY SKILLS: research skills

1 Read the texts (1–5) and decide what type of information each text is giving. Choose from the following:

A specific information   B general info

C opinion   D character

1

John Cody Fidler-Simpson CBE

(*born 9 August 1944*) is an English foreign correspondent. He is world affairs editor of BBC News, the world's biggest broadcast news service. One of the most travelled reporters ever, he has spent all his working life at the corporation. He has reported from more than 120 countries, including 30 war zones, and has interviewed numerous world leaders.

2 Simpson's reporting career includes the following episodes:-

• He travelled back from Paris to Tehran with the exiled Ayatollah Khomeini on 1 February 1979, a return that heralded the Iranian Revolution, as millions lined the streets of the capital.

• In 1989 he dodged bullets at the Beijing Tiananmen Square massacre.

• Simpson reported the fall of Ceaucescu regime in Bucharest later that year.

• He spent the early part of the 1991 Gulf War in Baghdad, before being expelled by the authorities.

• Simpson reported from Belgrade during the Kosovo War of 1999, where he was one of a handful of journalists to remain in the Serbian capital after the authorities, at the start of the conflict, expelled those from NATO countries.

• Two years later, he was one of the first reporters to enter Kabul in the 2001 US-led invasion of Afghanistan.

• He was the first BBC journalist to answer questions in a war zone from Internet users via BBC News Online.

3

John Simpson

Journalists, in the BBC and elsewhere, have come to accept that where a big story is breaking, John Simpson will probably be there first.

In the competitive world of foreign affairs reporting, a nose for the right place at the right time is invaluable. John Simpson's remarkable gut instincts have drawn him into the thick of the action time and time again, and earned him scoops which are the envy of his colleagues. He has witnessed 30 years of upheaval in all corners of the globe, but John Simpson has no thoughts of retiring. 'It's a way of life,' he says.

4

DavidA: How do you stay so positive when you see so many awful happenings?

JS: Well, the fact is that people – a lot of people – behave really well when the moment comes. I mean, not everybody, in fact, not in any sense the majority, but there's always people in every circumstance … I did some reporting on that awful, awful massacre in Rwanda in 1994, when people behaved bestially to their friends and neighbours of different tribes, but I also met people who behaved with the most tremendous courage in rescuing, saving and protecting their neighbours of a different ethnic group. When you see that – that was just one thing, but I've seen it in so many other places around the world. In Bosnia for instance, where sometimes I used to think people behaved dreadfully, and yet some people behaved so well.

I feel that just a few people behaving properly and decently gives you a feeling that the whole of humanity is saved.

ALion12: What drives you to risk your life to report from the front line?

JS: Well for a start I don't necessarily see it as risking my life; we've got a lot of good protection and a lot of really good security people working for us, which means you don't even have to worry or think about it. I just want to tell people what's going on. I want to find out for myself what's going on, I want to know. With Bosnia, I wanted to go there, examine how well it was doing and make my own mind up; I don't want somebody else telling me. And that's what I did.

5 The reason may be that the audience trusts and respects him. Television news does not overflow with wisdom; Simpson appears wise. Television does, on the other hand, often overflow with certainty; Simpson is the first to appear uncertain. He looks reflective, a thinker in a complicated world, and yet comfortable and ordinary.

2 Read the texts about John Simpson again. Which are reliable sources? For each of the ones you mark unreliable, give reasons why.

	Reliable?	Why unreliable?
Text 1		
Text 2		
Text 3		
Text 4		
Text 5		

> **WRITING SKILLS: writing a features article for a magazine or newspaper**

3 Read the beginnings of a features article on John Simpson. Match the styles (A–D) with the articles (1–4).

A quote   C anecdote

B summary   D surprising statement

1 Do you like a walk in the park on a Sunday? Maybe time spent with family and friends taking it easy? Not John Simpson. An ideal Sunday for him would be stuck behind a wall somewhere with his cameraman while the bullet are flying around.

_____

2 John Simpson has, for the last forty years, been one of the best war correspondents in the BBC. Having attended more than thirty war situations …

_____

3 'I just want to tell people what's going on' says John Simpson when asked about the reasons why he keeps sending himself to the most dangerous places in the world. _____

4 John Simpson loves to tell everyone about his first interview, which was with the then Prime Minister, Harold Wilson, when the PM punched him in the stomach for asking a rude question.

_____

4 Use one of the beginnings 1–4 above and information from the texts. Write a short features article on John Simpson.

_____

_____

_____

_____

_____

_____

_____

_____

9 Law and society

9.1 HIDDEN RULES

VOCABULARY: words from the lesson

1 Match 1–9 with a–e to make complete verb phrases.

1 bring something	a) and dance about something
2 draw attention	b) dirty linen in public
3 know something is	c) to a halt
4 make a	d) responsibilities
5 make a song	e) to yourself
6 mind your	f) for granted
7 shirk your	g) amiss
8 take something	h) scene
9 wash your	i) own business

EXTRA VOCABULARY: collocations

2 Match the verb phrases in Exercise 1 with the situations A-I.

A Because the soldier didn't stay awake when he was on duty, the enemy gained entry and took the castle.

B The minister felt uncomfortable when he attended the meeting. He felt sure that they had already decided to sack him.

C Sarah didn't like her boyfriend asking questions about her.

D Paul can always be found at parties telling everyone about the latest problems in his love life.

E After spending more than 16 million pounds on the project, the government felt that it was no longer worthwhile.

F He was so sure he had passed the exam, so imagine the shock when he found out he had failed!

G In such situations it is best to keep a low profile and then you won't be asked to do anything.

H My daughter never accepts no as an answer. She'll start screaming immediately.

I It was a simple mistake but his wife has now been talking about it for thirty minutes.

---

3 Write in the word that collocates with the following words.

1 welfare / health / justice _____

2 anti-social / criminal / bad _____

3 _____ development / collapse / migrant

4 ban / permit / restrict _____

5 repeal / break / create _____

6 _____ unemployment / crime/ culture

4 Use collocations from Exercise 3 and other collocations to complete the text.

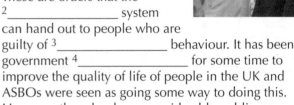

There has been pressure recently to
¹_____ the law that created ASBOs. These are orders that the ²_____ system can hand out to people who are guilty of ³_____ behaviour. It has been government ⁴_____ for some time to improve the quality of life of people in the UK and ASBOs were seen as going some way to doing this. However, there has been considerable public ⁵_____ recently with people complaining that ASBOs are being used specifically to target the working ⁶_____. However, many have defended the use of ASBOs as they have been particularly good at restricting attacks against economic ⁷_____ and cutting down on youth ⁸_____.

TRANSLATION

5 Translate the idioms into your own language.

1 _____

2 _____

3 _____

4 _____

5 _____

6 _____

7 _____

8 _____

9 _____

VOCABULARY: justice systems

1 Complete the blog with words from the box.

community	custodial	care	deter
deterrent	delinquency	punishment	
offenders	rehabilitation	courts	

NANNY HENRY SPEAKS OUT!

By the time that young ¹_____ reach the youth ²_____, it is probably already too late to ³_____ them from crime in the future. After all, where is ⁴_____ and recovery to come from now their parents are not respected enough to support them? It won't come from ⁵_____ service. Teenagers just resent it. And it won't come from ⁶_____ care as that is pretty much the same as prison and we know how helpful THAT is.

It is the parents' ⁷_____ system: how they support, reward and punish their child, that is the best ⁸_____ to juvenile ⁹_____. If parents can find the right ¹⁰_____ to teach their children early enough the error of their ways, then teenage crime will dramatically decrease.

READING

2a Tick (✓) the correct age group for each piece of advice. Some advice can be used for more than one age group.

	0–2	3–5	6–8
a) record behaviour to plan how to punish or reward			
b) establish your authority			
c) make sure you punish or reward when you said you would			
d) model good behaviour			
e) use timeouts			
f) give specific praise			
g) clearly say 'No'			
h) tell your kids what is the right way first			
i) always set a good example			
j) tell kids the rules			

2b Read the article on page 62 and check your answers to Exercise 2a.

3 Read the article again and match the situations 1–4 with the advice in Exercise 2a.

1 The first time your child uses crayons to decorate the living room wall, discuss why that's not allowed and what will happen if your child does it again. ____

2 Saying 'I'm proud of you for sharing your toys at playgroup' is usually more effective than punishing a child for the opposite behaviour — not sharing. ____

3 Instead of saying 'Don't jump on the couch,' try 'Please sit on the furniture and put your feet on the floor.' ____

4 'Slam that door and you'll never watch TV again!' ____

GRAMMAR: adverbs of degree

4 Find all the adverbs of degree in the article on page 62 and add them to the table.

Adverbs used with gradeable adjectives	Adverbs used with ungradeable adjectives

5 Add at least two more adverbs of degree to each column.

6 Rewrite the following sentences using the correct adverbs of degree and a suitable adjective from the box. Make any other necessary changes.

unacceptable	qualified	essential
lucky	unlikely	

1 She has too many qualifications for this post.

She is _____.

2 There was a little luck to his getting a promotion.

He was _____.

3 I don't think you have succeeded in answering the question at all.

Your response is _____.

4 I think there is little chance he will be arrested.

It is _____ be arrested.

5 It really is necessary for you to be there.

It is _____ for you to be there.

How to discipline your child

How do you keep a one-year-old from trying to turn on your DVD player? What should you do when your preschool child has a tantrum? How can you get a teenager to respect your authority?

Whatever the age of your child, it's extremely important to be consistent when it comes to discipline. If parents don't follow the rules and consequences they set up, their children aren't likely to either.

Here are some ideas about how to vary your approach to discipline to best fit your family.

Ages 0 to 2

When your crawling baby or energetic toddler heads towards an unacceptable or dangerous toy, calmly say 'No' and either remove your child from the area or distract him or her with an appropriate activity.

Timeouts can be a really effective discipline for toddlers. A child who has been hitting, biting, or throwing food, for example, should be told why the behaviour is unacceptable and taken to a designated timeout area — a kitchen chair or bottom stair — for a minute or two to calm down (longer timeouts are not effective for toddlers).

It's important not to smack, hit, or slap a child of any age. Babies and toddlers are hardly likely to be able to make any connection between their behaviour and physical punishment. They will only feel the pain of the hit.

And don't forget that kids learn by watching adults, particularly their parents. Make sure your behaviour is role-model material. It is utterly ridiculous to expect your child to pick up toys while your stuff is left all over the place!

Ages 3 to 5

As your child grows and begins to understand the connection between actions and consequences, make sure you start communicating the rules of your family's home.

Explain to kids what you expect of them **before** you punish them for a certain behaviour.

The earlier that parents establish this kind of 'I set the rules and you're expected to listen or accept the consequences' standard, the better for everyone. Consistency is the key to effective discipline, and it's important for parents to decide together (unless you are a single parent) what the rules are and then uphold them.

Don't underestimate the positive effect that your praise can have — discipline is not just about punishment but also about recognizing good behaviour. And be specific when giving praise; don't just say, 'Good job!'

If your child continues showing unacceptable behaviour no matter what you do, try making a chart with a box for each day of the week. Decide how many times your child can misbehave before a punishment starts or how long the proper behaviour must be displayed before it is rewarded. Once this begins to work, praise your child for learning to control misbehaviour and, especially, for overcoming any stubborn problem.

Timeouts also can work well for kids at this age. Establish a suitable timeout place that's free of distractions and will force your child to think about how he or she has behaved. Remember, sending your child to a room that has a computer or a TV is fairly sure to fail as a punishment. Don't forget to consider the length of time that will best suit your child.

It's important to tell kids what the right thing to do is, not just to say what the wrong thing is.

Ages 6 to 8

Timeouts and consequences are also really effective discipline strategies for this age group.

Again, consistency is absolutely crucial, as is follow-through. Keep any promises of discipline or else you risk undermining your authority. Kids have to believe that you mean what you say. This is not to say you can't give second chances or allow a certain margin of error, but for the most part, you should act on what you say.

Be careful not to make unrealistic threats of punishment in anger, since not sticking to what you say could weaken **all** your threats.

LISTENING

7 | 2.8 | **Listen to the first part of a talk about discipline and complete the notes.**

1 Rewards are better known to psychologists as
_____.

2 A monthly pay slip is another example of
_____

3 In this case 'negative' means taking away
_____

4 Nagging is not a punishment but a promise that
_____ if the behaviour is stopped.

5 We take aspirin _____ something bad, in this case, a headache.

6 A positive punishment is doing something
_____ to stop something else happening.

8 | 2.9 | **Listen to the second part of the talk and answer the following questions.**

1 What two reasons are given about why smacking is a bad thing?

a) _____

b) _____

2 What is the advantage of 'timeouts'?

_____

1a 2.10 **Listen and write what you hear.**

_____

_____

_____

_____

_____

_____

1b **Read what you have written and answer the questions.**

1 Where would you expect to see this information?

    a) a brochure

    b) a course guide

    c) a pamphlet

    d) an article

2 What is the best title for the text?

    a) Places in the international community

    b) How communities integrate into UK life

    c) Turks: how are they different?

    d) Growing up away from home

When I was in the sixth form, one of my tutors told me: 'Well done, you've learnt a lot of English this year.'
Of course, he meant it as a compliment. But it was a bit of a shock.
It was only then that it really hit me that my language skills were not great. I was born here, English was my language, but my vocabulary was poor because of the environment I grew up in.
The Turkish community in London is populated with a lovely bunch of hard-working, friendly people. But they have suffered from not really integrating.
My father, Hassan, came over in the 60s, a grill chef just looking for work, not really wanting to stay.
But time passed, his wife, Emine, came to join him and they ended up in Haringey in north-east London, running a fish and chip shop that also did kebabs.
A few of his cousins came over at the same time as him. Every year others joined them – all from the same fishing village in Turkey – all to the same part of London.
Over the years they travelled back to visit their village near Trabzon on the Black Sea. And they used money earned in foreign countries – England, Germany and others, to invest in the land of their fathers for when they go home.
I've been there and I've seen the changes that pounds, deutschmarks and Euros have made.
In London, all the Trabzon Turks are clustered around the Green Lanes area of Haringey. The main road is a typical Victorian London street, lined with Turkish shops, food stores, jewellery stores and restaurants.
If you visit one of the many cafés you'll find Turkish men – and unfortunately it is mainly men – gathering. They drink 'chai', play 'tavla' – that's backgammon – and discuss their lives.
Unfortunately, the community is quite inward-looking. One reason may be that they have a different culture, tradition and religion. Some of these values are good – hard work, respect for elders. But their values are those of 1960s Turkey. The UK has changed a lot in that time, and Turkey has changed, too.
They also see the worst of British life. Many of them work in kebab shops. They see drunken teens pouring in after a night out on the town, shouting at staff.
They don't want to see their children like that, and it makes them guard their values more closely.

And language is a big issue. I believe the most important thing for immigrant communities is to learn the lingo. With language comes an understanding of culture and tradition. Even if you don't like something, you can understand it better if you know the language.
However, my parents were typical. My dad learnt a little English and he encouraged my mother to do the same. But she was shy, and found it difficult to carry on. So, like many women in the community, my mum learnt a few words to shop and get by. They don't need to speak English in their daily lives with friends, relatives, and neighbours who speak Turkish.
Growing up in that community, I had a few more restrictions than the average young kid here. I didn't stay out clubbing until two or three in the morning, until I went to university. There were no girlfriends for me or my brothers nor boyfriends for my sisters when we were teens. I feel British. My past and my future is here.
But I guess many of my parents' generation don't think of themselves as English. They are Turkish and just happen to be living here, they long to go back to Trabzon.
Even some people of my age say they don't feel British. And I argue with them. I believe the ones who venture out win. I've gained much more by being with other cultures and traditions.
And maybe my experience of venturing out of the community can be inspirational to some.

2 Read the text on page 63 and tick (✓) the things that are true about Huseyin Oz and the Turkish community.

1 His teacher thought he wasn't English. ☐

2 The community he grew up in are all from the same place in Turkey. ☐

3 They worked in England to build a future there. ☐

4 The community tries hard to adapt to British culture. ☐

5 Older Turkish people do not like all aspects of British culture. ☐

6 His mother only learnt enough English to survive. ☐

7 His childhood was different to other British kids. ☐

8 He feels similar to all second generation Turkish people in Great Britain. ☐

GRAMMAR: reporting using nouns

3 Rewrite the comments as reported speech, using backshift at all times.

1 All the people in my family come from the same part of Turkey.

2 Many migrants came to the UK and set up shops.

3 Migrants work in the UK but hope to go home one day.

4 The UK and Turkey have both changed a lot.

5 The Turks are a very strong community.

6 British culture does not always provide good examples of how to live.

7 Young people with Turkish parents feel British.

1 *Huseyin said that all the people in his family's part of London had come from the same part of Turkey.*

2 _____

3 _____

4 _____

5 _____

6 _____

7 _____

4 Rewrite the following sentences using the noun form of the underlined words.

1 She had no right to <u>accuse</u> me of cheating.
_____ she made about me cheating was unfair.

2 They <u>advise</u> you to attend an English course as soon as you arrive but I already speak English.
_____ to attend an English course was not useful.

3 Although he <u>denied</u> entering the country illegally, they didn't believe him.
_____ was not believed.

4 They have finally <u>agreed</u> to stop arguing about the course programme.
_____ arguing about the course programme has been reached.

5 She <u>explained</u> each stage of the experiment clearly.
_____ of the experiment was very clear.

6 When he <u>observed</u> that no one had been guarding the entrance, I was astonished.
_____ was astonishing.

KEY LANGUAGE:
balancing an argument

1 Match 1–7 with a–g to make sentences.

1 Having said that, vandalism is against the law,

2 Certainly talking to the police is important

3 While accepting that it is a community issue,

4 I see what you're saying

5 Although we're here to talk about the cultural fair,

6 Admittedly, talking to the police

7 That's all fair enough, but

a) would be helpful.

b) I think that we should start by talking about violence on our streets.

c) but don't you think we should talk to the police?

d) it's simply too dangerous.

e) we mustn't forget it's a crime.

f) but I still think that we need to get the parents involved.

g) it isn't solely about having fun and causing accidental damage.

2 Complete the dialogue with sentences from Exercise 1.

A: Good morning everyone. _____

_____

We need to take action. I think we need to call the parents in.

B: I'm not so sure. _____

_____

A: _____

After all, it's their kids that are causing the problems.

C: _____

Police involvement is crucial.

A: _____

However, this is a local community issue and we should deal with it ourselves.

C: _____

We live in this country and must respect the law.

A: _____

we go to the police and give them the names, our community won't trust us anymore.

C: That's a price we'll have to pay. I'm sure they'll understand.

STUDY SKILLS:
synthesising information

1 Read quotations 1–4 and match them to the notes A and B.

1 'When immigrants find themselves classed as second-class citizens and constantly reminded that they are not "one of us", they will re-identify more strongly with their home culture and identity. This is why often immigrants may become more stereotypical than the other members of their family back home or return to their home country quickly.' ☐

2 'With the arrival, particularly of Polish migrants after 2003, the British economy received a massive boost. Companies who were having problem with staffing found that they were filling all their posts with highly motivated workers. Profits rose by more than 6 percent and economic growth was witnessed at similar levels. It would be fair to term the Polish migrant revolution as the greatest example of Polish-British cooperation since the Battle of Britain.' ☐

3 'With government support, many communities were able to receive funding to open their own schools. In the last fifteen years, over 350 schools have opened, providing for the Turkish, Polish, Greek, Russian and Arabic speaking children.' ☐

4 'A native citizen is more likely to have choices and also to have higher expectations from a job than an immigrant. Migrants will be more motivated as their situation is very much "life or death" as they cannot often rely on families and friends. This results in migrants working for less money and yet being more ambitious than the native citizen.' ☐

A

Faro, 2008 The community within:
how host countries
fail migrants

- migrants facing major
problems when moving to
another country
- research shows that migrants
will work harder for less pay.
Results in more success for
companies they work for.
- 22 percent of migrants
return home within 3 years.
- increase in vandalism and
physical violence on and from
the immigrant communities
- lack of government
programme mean language
problems and failure to
culturally integrate.

B

- Griffiths, Sons and Daughter
of Migrants: the future of all
of us 2005
- second generation immigrants
train parents in new culture and
close the culture gap
- government attempting to
support immigrants' children
through education
- multicultural society evolving
in Britain giving a good example
to other countries who will face
such issues in the future
over 25,000 immigrant children
born every year in England
alone.

WRITING SKILLS:
a literature review

2a Look at the information in Exercise 1 again and fill in the gaps 1–5 paragraphs A–I below with the correct phrases a)–e).

a) Faro also observes

d) has examined

b) According to Faro,

e) In Griffith's view

c) Griffiths touches on

A Faro focuses on the problems that migrants have when they first come to the host country, whereas Griffiths concentrates on second generation migrants. ☐

B They have also been very successful in strengthening the British economy. It seems unlikely the country would have developed its economy so fast without this sudden influx of workers. ☐

C 1___ the growth of the second generation of communities in the UK and argues that it is growing fast, leading to a much more multicultural society in the UK. ☐

D 2___, there are major problems for migrants when they first arrive in the community. The failure of the government to provide cultural integration and language programmes results in migrants identifying even more with their home country. ☐

E She also counters Faro's accusation that the government is not doing enough for the communities by focusing on the efforts to improve education in the communities. ☐

F 3___ that migrant workers are much more motivated to work than a citizen of the home country. ☐

G Faro 2008 and Griffith 2005 approach the issue of the migrant communities from two different directions. ☐ 1

H Griffiths 4___ the cultural crisis in the community but disagrees with Faro. 5___, children of the second generation can do a lot to close the gaps between the two communities. ☐

I Both of them come to very different conclusion about the migrant communities. ☐

2b Number paragraphs A–I above in the correct order.

3 Match the ideas in the four quotations in Exercise 1 with four of the paragraphs A–I above.

1 ___   2 ___   3 ___   4 ___

10 Arts and entertainment

10.1 PERFORMANCE

VOCABULARY: words from the lesson

1a Reorder the letters to make words from Lesson 10.1 of the Coursebook.

1 neveu _____

2 roihc _____

3 libl _____

4 datatniopa _____

5 napymoc _____

6 riot _____

7 suotoriv _____

8 gopherchreorar _____

1b Use the words from Exercise 1a to complete the text.

Tonight, at that superb [1]_____, the Witherall Centre, Paul Astaire tops the [2]_____ with Jenny Ayre and Paulo Morelli. The three of them make up the [3]_____ the Tapping Toes. Paul is also the [4]_____ of the troupe coming up with superb dance routines, the best being 'Dancing in the Snow', an [5]_____ of the great Gene Kelly number. Paul Astaire, left the Wilbur [6]_____ last year to do more work on his own. This dance [7]_____ is a must-see as he is very rarely in the UK now, even if you have to put up with the truly awful Willesden [8]_____, possibly the worst group of singers I have ever heard.

2a Match the words from the box with the words 1–8 to make compound adjectives.

born	heavy	inspiring	packed
studded	the-way	trained	winning

1 star _____

2 awe _____

3 professionally _____

4 fun _____

5 medal _____

6 French _____

7 out-of _____

8 top _____

2b Use the compound adjectives from Exercise 2a to complete the sentences.

1 His house is so _____ that you'll never find it without a map.

2 The trick of jumping 400 metres without a parachute and landing on his feet was truly _____.

3 Caroline is a better dancer because she is _____. I only go to classes at weekends.

4 The _____ footballer can play for England because his mother was born in Lowestoft.

5 This _____ party game will get you acting, miming, singing and dancing in no time.

6 Ali Al-Badawi is the country's first _____ athlete at this year's Olympics.

7 The _____ show features actors and singers from all the top musicals.

8 The tower was so _____ when it was built that it started leaning and it was no surprise when it eventually fell down.

DICTATION

1a 2.11 **Listen and write what you hear.**

_____

_____

_____

_____

_____

_____

_____

1b **Read what you have written and answer the questions.**

1 What were the causes of the Dust Bowl?

_____

2 What were the effects of the Dust Bowl?

_____

3 Which man best understood the Dust Bowl period?

_____

LISTENING

2 2.12 **Listen to the talk about life of Woody Guthrie and put the following events in order.**

a) Mother could no longer speak. ☐

b) Woody was very affected by the suffering of the workers. ☐

c) Family lived in Oklahoma. ☐

d) Woody learned to play the harmonica. ☐

e) Woody left home and travelled to Texas. ☐

f) Woody wrote his most famous song. ☐

g) Woody became politically active. ☐

h) The beginning of the Dust Bowl years. ☐

i) Woody's songs were broadcast on the radio. ☐

j) He learned to play the guitar. ☐

k) His sister died. ☐

l) Woody went to California. ☐

3 2.12 **Listen again and answer the questions.**

1 What made it easier for Woody to understand the plight of the Dust Bowl refugees?

_____

2 What makes songs in a farming community different from songs on the radio?

_____

3 Why did Woody travel by train? (two reasons)

_____

4 Why was going to California such a disappointment for the refugees? (two reasons)

_____

GRAMMAR: non-finite clauses

4 2.12 **Listen again and complete the following excerpts.**

1 _____ of Oklahoma in 1912, Woody Guthrie not only came to represent ...

2 _____ in the farming town of Oklahoma, Guthrie was able to experience.

3 _____ of his family life, Woody turned to music.

4 _____ with others difficult, Woody preferred to communicate through his music.

5 _____ the farming community, the lack of rain at this time heralded the Dust Bowl period.

6 _____, his legacy still lives on in the works of diverse singers and groups as ...

5 **Rewrite the following sentences with non-finite clauses.**

1 It took us a long time before we understood what the film was about.

_____

2 The aim of the project is to encourage potential violinists to train with virtuosos.

_____

3 He uses lighter colours so that the observer feels calm and positive.

_____

4 If it can be financed by a wealthy sponsor, the show should be successful.

_____

5 The play ran in the West End for two years and made a profit of more than four million pounds.

_____

READING

6 Read the article and tick (✓) the correct sentences.

1 The text is a review of a DVD. ☐

2 The writers admires Woody greatly. ☐

3 The collection is valuable mainly as a historical document. ☐

4 The collection includes both songs and interviews. ☐

5 Woody rarely played the same song the same way. ☐

6 Woody's songs can be funny in an ironic way. ☐

7 Whenever he speaks, Woody's opinions on life come through clearly. ☐

EXTRA VOCABULARY: words from the text

7 Find words in the article that mean the following:

1 the quality of something being expressed clearly _____

2 very frightening or shocking and making you feel very upset _____

3 filled with a particular meaning, quality, or sound _____

4 making a long high sound _____

5 things that are completely stupid or unreasonable _____

6 to stop oneself from showing feeling _____

7 quiet laughs _____

8 problems and difficulties _____

DUST BOWL BALLADS

Perhaps the lone salvation of human tragedy is that occasionally it finds its poet, the one person who lends meaning to suffering and rescues dignity from disaster. The Dust Bowl crisis of the Thirties found its poet in Woody Guthrie, as the recently re-released Library of Congress Recordings and *Dust Bowl Ballads* demonstrate with overwhelming clarity.

The Library of Congress Recordings are particularly remarkable. The three-record set, which was recorded for a radio show in 1940 at a studio owned by the government, runs nearly three hours. It consists of Guthrie performing twenty-eight songs during the course of an interview with musicologist Alan Lomax and Lomax's wife, Elizabeth Littleton.

In response to Lomax's questions, Guthrie, who was born in 1912, chronicles his harrowing family life in Oklahoma, his days of 'hoboin' and his experiences with the Okies who travelled the hard road to the promised land of California. His songs weave in and out of the conversation.

Guthrie seems incapable of discussing a subject without striking a resonant moral chord. Early on he drifts into talking about 'the coloured situation' and tells how he came upon a wailing harmonica instrumental he calls *Railroad Blues*. He first heard the piece, he tells Lomax, while walking past a barbershop in Oklahoma as a young black man played it. Guthrie describes the tune as 'undoubtedly the lonesomest piece of music that I ever run into in my life.' He asked the man where he learned it. 'I just lay here and listen to the railroad whistle,' the man explained, 'and whatever it say, I say too.' 'He never did play the same piece no two days alike,' Guthrie says of the man, 'and he called them all *Railroad Blues*!'

In the Dust Bowl migrations, Guthrie discovered his own version of the blues, one on which he'd play endless variations. As Southern and Great Plains states became unliveable because of drought and the Depression, California came to seem like the land of milk and honey to desperate farmers. In song after song – *Talking Dust Bowl Blues*, *I Ain't Got No Home*, *Will Rogers Highway* – Guthrie captures the hopelessness of the crop and bank failures, the rigours of the journey west and the disappointment that ensued when California offered a reality nearly as harsh as the land left behind.

Horrifying as the situation was, Guthrie was capable of perceiving the absurdities of it. In *Do-Re-Mi* he can barely suppress his chuckles as he advises westward-bound refugees that 'California is a garden of Eden/A paradise to live in or to see/But believe it or not/You won't find it so hot/If you ain't got the do-re-mi.' Such tough knowledge doesn't prevent him, however, from being obviously moved some time later as he describes an old man hitching to California and refusing to believe that his hardships are not about to end.

Among its fourteen superb selections, *Dust Bowl Ballads* offers better-recorded versions of many of the songs on the Library of Congress Recordings, without the conversation. Because of the circumstances under which it was made, the three-record set, unlike *Dust Bowl Ballads*, the quality is not so good. Also, Guthrie occasionally makes false starts, hits bum notes and goes out of tune in this one-take setting. Still, the substance and historical import of the Library of Congress Recordings by far outweigh its technical shortcomings. And, to emphasise a point that was made when Bruce Springsteen, U2 and Bob Dylan paid tribute to Guthrie on *Folkways: A Vision Shared* last year, the importance of Guthrie's music is not exclusively historical. The lessons his songs teach are essential in a time that has its own problems with homelessness, displaced workers, bank failures and farm crises.

As usual, Woody said it best. 'Wherever people ain't free/Wherever men are fightin' for their rights,' he sings in *Tom Joad – Part 2*, on *Dust Bowl Ballads*, 'That's where I'm a-gonna be.' That's as true now, more than forty years after Woody Guthrie's death, as it ever was.

READING

1 Read the leaflet and answer the questions.

12.00 - Main Exhibition Hall

Panel Discussion

Dr Mancini
Dr Sally Bernard
Dr Victor Cherkov
Erica Winters
The panel discussion will focus on the very
contentious issue of the role of video games in
society. Are they a source for good or evil?
The panel will explore the issues and also consider
the more recent explosion in online gaming
and question whether this has
resulted <u>in moving
the goalposts</u>
somewhat.

1 Has this leaflet come from

   a) a university course?

   b) a conference?

   c) a training course?

2 What does the underlined idiom mean?

   a) rebuilding something

   b) changing the conditions of something

   c) making things more difficult

LISTENING

2 2.13 Listen to a panel discussion and answer the following questions.

1 What is the first question?

_____

2 How many people believe that they can see benefits?

_____

3 Who believes that the panel is not focusing on the real issue?

_____

3 2.13 Listen again and decide who said what.

A Dr Sally Bernard

B Dr Mancini

C Dr Victor Cherkov

D Erica Winters

1 There are not enough controls on computer games. ____

2 Computer games may teach children skills that they will need in their lives ____

3 More adults play online games than children. ____

4 More information needs to be provided to families about computer games. ____

5 Companies do care who plays the game. ____

6 Parents are wrong to be frightened of brain damage to children. ____

7 Buyers should be checked if they are old enough to play the games. ____

8 Educational bodies should be using computer games more. ____

9 Computer games are more profitable than CDs and DVDs. ____

10 Some violent crimes have been linked to violent computer games. ____

GRAMMAR: spoken English

4 2.14 Listen to the excerpts A–H from the panel discussion and match them to the descriptions. Look at the audioscripts for Track 2.14 on page 95 to help you.

1 overlaps ____

2 listener responses – supportive comments ____

3 hesitation ____

4 repetition of words and phrases ____

5 discourse markers to give a speaker time to organise his/her thoughts ____

6 simple clause structure, adding clauses to each other, often independent clauses or simple dependent clauses ____

7 ellipsis ____

8 reformulations ____

5 Rewrite the sentences to show the feature of spoken English in brackets. You may need to add or delete some words.

1 I showed you how to do it, didn't I? It's so easy, mate! (Ellipsis)

_____

2 The final conclusion was there wasn't enough funding to take a risk. (Reformulations)

_____

3 Many people think there is no practical way we can make this work. But I know we are able to. (Repetition)

_____

4 That's the not the right way. We should do it more carefully for example by checking the location first. (Discourse markers to give a speaker time to organise his/her thoughts)

_____

5 We can print a picture, write a poster on the computer, print them, post them on every wall. (Simple clause structure)

_____

READING

6 Complete the newspaper article with sentences A–F.

A There are massive, powerful industries promoting many play-like activities.

B The only determinant common to both female and male video-game players was greater reliance on the Internet for social support.

C She suggests that many video games are different enough from original forms of play that they may be better defined as 'play-like activities.'

D Participants reported whether they were players or non-players, and weekly usage was collected.

E The data illustrates the need for further research among adults to clarify how to use digital opportunities more effectively in order to promote health and prevent disease.

F Immersion in media environments was evaluated using the participants' estimates of the time they spent during a typical week surfing the Internet and watching TV, including videos and DVDs.

New Study Finds Links Between Video-Game Playing And Health Risks In Adults

While video gaming is generally perceived as a pastime for children and young adults, research shows that the average age of players is 35. The Centre for Disease Control and Prevention (CDC), distributed questionnaires all over the word and finally analysed data from over 500 adults varying in age from 19 to 90 on health risks; media-use behaviours and perceptions, including those related to video-game playing; and demographic factors. They indicated measurable correlations between video-game playing and health risks. [1]____ Internet usage was assessed, as was the relative importance of the Internet as a social support. The personal determinants examined in this study included self-assessments of depression, personality, health status, physical and mental health, body mass index (BMI), and poor quality of life. [2]____

A total of 45.1 percent of respondents reported playing video games. Female video-game players reported greater depression and lower health status than female non-players. Male video-game players reported higher BMI and more Internet use time than male non-players. [3]____ Dr James Welling states, 'As hypothesised, health-risk factors – specifically, a higher BMI and a greater number of poor mental-health days – enable us to differentiate between adult video-game players and non-players. Video-game players also reported lower extraversion, consistent with research on adolescents that linked video-game consumption to a sedentary lifestyle and overweight status, and to mental-health concerns. Internet community support and time spent online distinguished adult video-game players from non-players, a finding consistent with prior research pointing to the willingness of adult video-game enthusiasts to sacrifice real-world social activities to play video games. [4]____,' Dr Brionny Allon praises Welling for identifying the current popularity of video games not only among youth, but also among adults. [5]____ She continues by saying, 'There are noteworthy differences between the oldest forms of play (e.g., chase games like hide and seek and tag) and today's "play-like activities." These play-like activities may stimulate the right centers of the brain to be engaging but erode other skills such as invention, social interaction, etc. The differences between today's "play-like activities" and original forms of play may reinforce some of the observed health-related conclusions made by Weaver, et al.' Dr. Allon believes that our greatest challenge will be maintaining the balance: 'How do we simultaneously help the public stay away from imitation play-like activities? [6]____ But who will be left to remind us that – for children and adults alike – Hide-And-Seek and Freeze Tag are still probably what we need most?'

KEY LANGUAGE:
an informal talk

1a Complete the sentences with the phrases from the box.

| before I forget then again anyway |
| and large kind of thing you know |
| all in all reckon that is |

a) By _____,TV shows don't have anywhere near the budget that films have got.

b) _____, that's my favourite programme right now.

c) I don't usually like that _____ but this show has a certain something.

d) _____, they are really human, not cardboard characters.

e) But _____, you already know that.

f) I _____ the best show on British TV is *Torchwood*.

g) So, _____ you expect that sci-fi programmes on TV are a bit basic.

h) _____, good guys always do good and bad guys are bad to the bone.

i) Oh, and _____, I better tell you when it's on.

1b Complete the text with the phrases from Exercise 1a.

¹___ That's my opinion anyway. I generally prefer crime shows. Yet, Torchwood is mystery and sci-fi put together. ²___ The good and bad guys in the show are not stereotypical. ³___ Not in *Torchwood*. Everyone has their strengths and weaknesses. ⁴___ And as for the effects, well they are really good for a TV show. Not just flashing light and bits of cardboard and plastic flying around. ⁵___ They've got million and millions of pounds to spend. TV programmes are lucky to have a million or so for the whole series, I suppose. ⁶___ But not *Torchwood*. The effects are really good.⁷___ I seriously recommend it. ⁸___ The best time to catch it is on Saturday at 7 p.m. but it's repeated on Tuesday at 7 p.m. on BBC3. ⁹___. I see you've already been checking the times!

STUDY SKILLS:
seminar / discussion skills

1 Read the following paragraph and describe the role of each sentence.

¹ Good afternoon everyone, my name is David Pierce and I will be running this seminar. ² This afternoon and Friday we will be looking at the influence of the struggle for independence on Anglo-Irish literature. ³ When I refer to independence, I mean the establishment of an independent Ireland in the 1920s, separate from Great Britain, and the creation of Northern Ireland, which remained with the British Kingdom. ⁴ Is everyone entirely clear on that?

1 _____

2 _____

3 _____

4 _____

2a Complete the conversation with words from the box.

| balance do you mean what you're saying |
| didn't catch that haven't heard from you |
| running out of put it well |
| see what you're going back to |

1 I understand _____, but …

2 We're _____ time, so …

3 I _____ getting at, but have …

4 When you say that, _____ that …

5 On_____, I think that …

6 Stefan _____ when he said …

7 … _____ what you said earlier, …

8 Lola, we _____ yet?

9 Sorry, I _____.

2b Match the first half of the phrases in Exercise 2a with the second half A–I.

A ... Patrick, I think you were referring to James Joyce, right? ____

B ... you think the Easter Rising did not change the opinions of Irish writers? ____

C ... can we just have one more question? ____

D ... Anglo-Irish literature was already developing fast and the struggle for independence had little effect. ____

E ... you considered the fact that Joyce wasn't in Ireland at the time? ____

F ... Could you say it again? ____

G ... What do you think of Emilia's opinion? ____

H ... your statement ignores the facts on the ground. Joyce couldn't be in two places at once. ____

I ... he thought that English literature could not have developed so much without the Irish renaissance. ____

WRITING SKILLS: creative writing (a screenplay)

3 Read the following text and turn it into a screenplay.

Sam closed the door and signalled to Diane to be quiet. He waited quietly behind the door until he heard the car driving away. Then, turning he suddenly screamed 'liar' at her! Dianne rocked back, as if she had been struck but when she asked him what he was talking about, Sam said nothing. He just walked to the window and looked out. Diane followed him across the room. 'You can't just shout at me like that and then pretend it never happened!' she cried to which he responded calmly that he could do whatever he liked. It was his house, after all. 'And I paid for it, Sam!' she replied. Sam, turned to his mother and asked her 'why didn't you tell me?' She asked him what good he thought it would do. 'After all, she continued, he's been in prison for fifteen years. He's not coming out anytime soon.' Suddenly, the phone rang. Sam crossed to the phone, picked it up and asked who was calling. He listened for a second and then he gasped. 'Who?' he asked. Immediately, Diane started to move to the phone 'If that's who I think it is' but Sam motioned for her to be quiet ...'

_____

_____

_____

_____

_____

_____

WRITE BETTER

Here are some tips for turning a narrative into a screenplay:

There are generally three types of text in a screenplay:

1 A description of the scene: this explains the scene and where everything is.
   e.g. A car park. There are three cars in the car park. A yellow ford is parked next to a blue Audi and an white Fiat in the centre of the car park.

2 Actions: this describes what things happen or what people do.
   e.g. Paul walks to the table, picks up the water jug and pours himself a glass. He drinks it slowly and then certainly smashes against the wall on the right in a fit of anger.

Note that both 1 and 2 are written in the present tense.

3 What people say: this may also include information on how they say it.e.g. Sarah: (sadly) I suppose you don't understand, do you?

Business and economics

11.1 UPS AND DOWNS

VOCABULARY: words from the lesson

1 Correct the phrases by rearranging the underlined words.

1 imports and <u>expenditure</u>

_____

2 mortgages and <u>liabilities</u>

_____

3 supply and <u>mergers</u>

_____

4 assets and <u>debtors</u>

_____

5 creditors and <u>slump</u>

_____

6 income and <u>demand</u>

_____

7 takeovers and <u>loss</u>

_____

8 boom and <u>exports</u>

_____

2 Match the phrases from Exercise 1 to the descriptions below.

a) After massive sales over the last six years we are now seeing a period where sales have hit rock bottom. ____

b) It was an aggressive bid for the company. However, if the bid is not accepted a joining of forces is considered. ____

c) There are too many things making the company a risk. The best idea is to sell off the profit-making sectors. ____

d) There are so many people ordering the new handbag that we just can't produce enough. ____

e) With no money in the company we have to call in the money that's owed to us so we can pay off those who invested in us. ____

f) To pay the interest on the house, we'll have to borrow some more money. ____

EXTRA VOCABULARY: trends

3 Look at the graphs and choose verbs from the box that best explain the trends being shown.

collapse	fluctuate	level off	plummet
reach a peak	stabilise	surge	take off

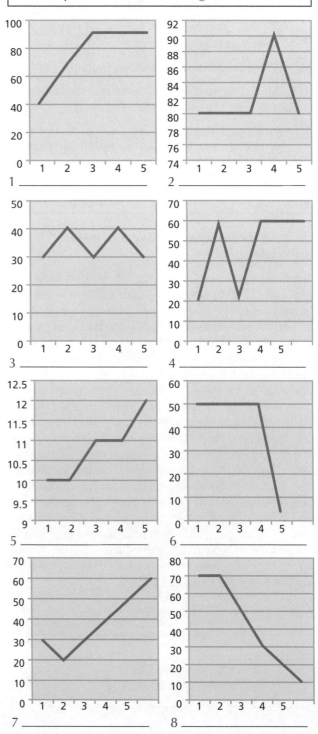

1 _____   2 _____

3 _____   4 _____

5 _____   6 _____

7 _____   8 _____

Crisis? What crisis?

It seems that not all of us were affected during the recent financial crisis. In fact, some countries haven't done badly at all. Here are just a few:

1 _____
I was surprised to learn that ¹____ may not be dramatically affected by the financial crisis. As it turns out, we in the West rely far more heavily on ¹____ than she does on us.
¹____ owns roughly 19 percent of US debts; if needed, it plans to use its sizable budget surplus to snap up even more. In addition, the West consumes the majority of ¹____-made goods, meaning a decrease in consumer demand here will make for a cool ¹____ export market.
However, ¹____ is not solely dependent on the West for financial stability. A host of new trade agreements mean ¹____ has a number of potential customers waiting for vast quantities of goods. Domestic demand is also on the up-and-up.
Finally, ¹____ financial system has been closed for many years, protecting it from shady assets. Though the country felt the international slump, its banking system is safe. Its high domestic demand, huge pile of capital, and numerous other major trading partners will counter the effects of the virus.
¹____ would be badly hurt by a downturn in export demand from the United States and Europe. It may yet be seriously affected. However, They can rely more on domestic demand and demand from less-affected countries, such as Brazil. They're also sitting on a mountain of cash, which they are using to borrow to the West.

2 _____
Latin American economies have busted over the past few years, becoming richer and more competitive. ²____, unlike some of its neighbours, stabilized its domestic economy while positioning itself for increased foreign investment. The United States is currently ²____ biggest trading partner, but is positioned to take advantage of trade agreements and foreign direct investment from India and China, two economies which have arisen to at the top of the world ladder.

3 _____
³____ banks have very little contact with international lenders. Therefore, any economic slowdown it feels will be a secondary result of global patterns. No shocks have occurred in the country itself and there are no threats, accept for its high exposure to the EU (especially Italy) and foreign direct investment which might subject ³____ to the general effects of the global recession. Known by its own journalists as the 'tiger of the east,' ³____ economy has preceded to grow rapidly for the past few years.
³____ is one of the world's biggest military equipment exporters. The country remains a hot destination for European companies looking to make investments. Its strong IT services sector—like a mini-India for the EU – is especially attractive. And then let's be honest, there is always a market for weapons in today's conflict-rich world society.

4 _____
AIG's (America's largest financial and insurance organization) gigantic ⁴____ subsidiary, AIA, has more than half of the ⁴____ market cornered. It's also sitting on about six billion pounds' worth of reserves and about eight billion pounds' worth of assets. A recent financial enquiry concluded, though, that ⁴____ would be susceptible to meltdown if there was any threat to AIG.
Foreigners affected directly by the financial crisis may have outstanding credits in ⁴____ which may negatively affect the ⁴____ market. The country, however, isn't worried, because the amount of these loans is relatively small. What must also be remembered is that ⁴____ is still a very rich country. They are literally sitting on a pile of cash.

5 _____
Driven by regional oil exports, ⁵____ boasts one of the world's fastest-growing economies. The UK's *Guardian* calls it the home of the 'Arabian Dream,' the world's new version of the spent American dream. ⁵____ free trade zone, superb commercial real estate market, and financial services make it an international powerhouse. This growth was fuelled by oil revenues, but now has a momentum of its own. ⁵____ international problems revolve more around illegal money transfers than the financial crisis yet ⁵____ has almost everything going for it. The place is booming.

READING

1 Read the article quickly and decide which of the following countries are being talked about in each paragraph.

> Brazil   UAE   Romania   China
> South Korea

2 Read the article again and decide which country …

1 has no major threats to its economy.

_____

2 relies on a market that never seems to go away.

_____

3 produces large amounts of consumer goods.

_____

4 hopes to be protected from threat by treaties with two other successful markets.

_____

5 has a lot of reserves to rely on. _____

6 is the best example in a region of high-flyers.

_____

7 seems to be growing without any outside influence.

_____

8 can actually make one other country's crisis worse.

_____

3 In the article on page 75 seven cases of the wrong word being used are underlined. Write the correct the word for each.

a) borrow _____

b) busted _____

c) arisen _____

d) accept _____

e) preceded _____

f) enquiry _____

g) credits _____

4 Complete the sentences with the correct form of the underlined words in the article on page 75.

1 I'm afraid I cannot _____ your generous offer.

2 _____ more money to pay off your debts is just stealing from Peter to pay Paul.

3 We knew the crisis had started when the National bank went _____.

4 There's enough _____ in my account to pay for the new equipment.

5 In response to your _____ I can assure you that your investment is safe.

6 The sudden fall in unemployment figures actually _____ the announcement that the economy had recovered.

7 The problem _____ because there hasn't been any quality check for the last three months.

LISTENING

5 2.15 Listen to the conversation and answer the questions.

1 Which countries do Danny and Raj agree on?

_____

2 Which countries do Danny and Raj disagree on?

_____

3 Which country does the article they are discussing not mention?

_____

6 2.15 Listen to the conversation again. Tick (✓) the people who make statements 1–6.

	Sally	Raj	Danny
1 A boom industry has now gone bust.			
2 You are only speaking about one country.			
3 I don't know enough about this market.			
4 The country has many different industries.			
5 The evidence is not entirely reliable.			
6 Many countries hope it doesn't realise its potential.			

GRAMMAR: alternatives to *if*

7a 2.15 Listen to the conversation again and write the alternatives to *if* in the order that you hear them.

1 _____   5 _____

2 _____   6 _____

3 _____   7 _____

4 _____

7b Complete the sentences with the alternatives to *if*.

1 _____ the government passed the motion now, it would still be too late to make a difference to the outcome.

2 _____ the intervention of the bank, the company would have been bankrupt.

3 _____ there's a last minute change, the press conference will take place at 10.

4 Bank managers will continue to give themselves pay rises _____ there is a financial crisis.

5 _____ there was an upward surge in the housing market, would that be good or bad for us?

6 They can have credit _____ they can pay the interest of 10 percent.

7 I would take out insurance _____ something goes wrong.

DICTATION

1 `2.16` Listen and write what you hear.

_____

_____

_____

_____

_____

_____

_____

READING

2 Read the article and match the headings A–J to the paragraphs 1–10.

A Small steps

B Exploring solutions

C Releasing the weak

D Creating normality

E Concessions for people

F Creating humanity

G Managing stress

H Developing authority

I The final assault

J Wearing them down

HOSTAGE NEGOTIATION

Once you have had time to assess the situation and you have gathered everything you need to know, what do you do?

Getting close

1 ____

In such a confused situation, the negotiator first tries to abolish chaos and panic and create calm. They talk in a calm voice and do a great deal of listening. In particular, they seek to create a space in which the hostage-takers can talk with the negotiator as reasonable people, much as you would talk with any normal person on the phone.

The negotiator is always there and always ready to talk. They will listen to everything and will try to eliminate bias so that reasonable negotiation can be conducted.

2 ____

Once normality is created, the negotiator listens uncritically to the hostage-taker, accepting them as they are and making them feel like humans, not criminals. They can then start discussing the hostages, how they are doing and whether they are unwell.

3 ____

The negotiator may also decide to put themselves in a position of power. This may start by being authoritative on behalf of the hostage-taker, for example in getting them communications and food. This may later extend to being authoritative with the hostage-taker. This can be a tricky and dangerous activity, as the hostage-taker wants to be in charge.

Developing the scene

4 ____

Progress may be slow, as trust and relationships continue to be built. Food and medicine may be permitted. Conversation with hostages may be instigated. Everyday chat creates normality.

Depending on the urgency of the situation, the negotiator may seek to speed up or slow down the talking. If hostages are hurt, then speed may be needed. If the hostage-takers

are requiring transport, or other things that would lead to more problems, then it may be better to make delays, such as saying you are 'looking into it' or asking kidnappers to clarify issues more clearly.

5 ____

Tension will continue throughout the negotiation. The negotiator may want to control this, reducing stress or increasing stress at different times.

6 ____ Eventually you will talk about how to resolve the situation. Of course the safe release of the hostages is always an important element.

The goal of the hostage-taker may be simply to escape and may be for publicity or other gain. If this is not acceptable to the authorities then other alternatives must be found.

Releasing the hostages

7 ____

Sometimes, just talk, talk, talk is enough to tire out the hostage-takers and for them to give themselves up. The ideal negotiation ends with the hostage-taker admitting defeat and agreeing to let everyone go, usually when the hostage-taker is exhausted. For this to happen, the negotiator must abstain at all times from letting their emotions get the better of them.

8 ____

Depending on the number of people taken hostage, a release of children, old people and those with medical conditions may be negotiated. It allows the hostage-takers to show that they are not 'bad' people after all.

9 ____

People may also be exchanged for various things, from food to publicity. When something is given to the hostage-takers, especially if it is on their list of demands, then the hostage-taker may be expected to donate a human as a sign of good faith.

10 ____

It is a very delicate balance for the negotiator when no clear exchange can be found and the hostage-takers look like they are going to kill hostages. The negotiator must notice the point at which the needs of the two sides collide and there is no way forward. This is when the armed forces take over. Even though some hostages may be killed, force may be the best solution to minimize damage or injury.

VOCABULARY: suffixes (nouns 2)

3 Put the underlined words in the article on p77 in the correct column to show how they can be turned into nouns.

-tion	-sion
	confusion

4 Use some of the words from Exercise 3 to complete the sentences.

1 We cannot act on the information until we have had _____ that it is reliable.

2 Her poor performance resulted in her _____ from the competition.

3 85 voted 'for', 75 voted 'against' and there were 13 _____.

4 Don't you need _____ before you can make that offer?

5 As we are a charity we have to rely on _____ to pay for our activities.

6 Since the _____ of the national ownership law, more foreign companies have been prepared to invest here.

7 At the _____ of the government minister, we started an internal inquiry.

8 The _____ by Hector Spinoza that he could not meet their demands, meant that the takeover could not take place.

LISTENING

5 2.17 Listen to the talk and complete the notes.

1 The hostage-taker must believe that _____ as much as they can from the negotiation.

2 You first offer should be _____ of your final offer.

3 A normal negotiation usually lasts no more than _____

4 A negotiation should move to _____, not a _____.

5 No new offer should be _____ from the last offer.

6 A hostage-taker should never feel that the negotiation was _____.

6 2.17 Listen to the talk again and tick (✓) the sentences that could be used in the listening text.

1 The first bid was 80,000 and the second was 100,000. ____

2 He thought he was a great negotiator because he got agreement on the first round. ____

3 The negotiator suggests 10,000 and when there's no agreement on that he increases it to 100,000. ____

4 As they couldn't come to agreement, the negotiator took him to court. ____

5 After the hostage-taker refused the 25,000 offer and demanded 75,000, the negotiator offered a compromise of 50,000. ____

6 It took Armando Alfaro six rounds to get agreement with the Hanson House terrorists. ____

GRAMMAR: phrasal verbs

7a Read the audioscript for Track 2.17 on page 95 and make a list of all the phrasal verbs mentioned. The first part is given to help you.

talk _____

go _____

hand _____

walk _____

draw _____

give _____

leave _____

speed _____

slow_____

7b Underline the phrasal verbs in the list that can have an object between the verb and particle.

KEY LANGUAGE:
setting the agenda and responding to offers

1 Read the dialogue and answer the question.

What are the three areas that are discussed?

- _____

- _____

- _____

A: All right, thank you for joining us. At this afternoon's session [1]_____ a timetable for the takeover.

B: I'm sorry, we're not clear about the details yet. [2]_____ what should be done about the assets and the liabilities.

A: [3]_____. Where do you want to start?

B: Let's start with the liabilities. It seems to us that you employ too many people and about 200 people will need to be laid off. This will mean redundancy payments which we will expect you to cover.

A: [4]_____. We don't agree with your estimates. We think no more than 45 staff need to be made redundant.

B: All right. Supposing we were to pay the redundancy of 100 staff, would you be willing to pay for the remaining hundred?

A: Sorry but we can't agree that. This is purely your decision.

B: OK, let's come back to that. We are also unhappy with the outstanding loans of 200 million pounds the company has. We would expect you to pay all of this off before the takeover. [5]_____ invest in your company unless it is clear of debt.

A: Well, I fail to see what we are getting out of this. Your bid was already low. [6]_____ the terms you offer if you also expect us to pay off the debts *and* the redundancies.

B: Hmm. OK. We'll increase our offer by 100 million as long as you pay off the debt.

A: [7]_____. However, we were hoping for a bit more from you, especially on the redundancies.

B: Fine. Then we will have to take a step back and consider only a 50 percent buyout in the first year and then consider a future full buyout later.

A: [8]_____ a much higher stake than that. 75 percent is the minimum we could consider.

B: I think you would need to convince us of your assets a little more before we could consider that …

2 Complete the dialogue in Exercise 1 with the following phrases A–H.

A Sounds OK to me.

B We're not happy about …

C Let's talk about …

D Yes, that's fine.

E I propose we discuss …

F I'm sorry, we were looking for …

G Well, I'm sorry. That's not acceptable.

H We're not prepared to …

3 Complete the table with examples from the text.

Making concessions	Accepting an offer	Rejecting an offer

STUDY SKILLS:
making a business presentation

1 `2.18` **Listen to the introduction to a presentation and answer the following questions.**

1 Where is it taking place?

_____

2 Who is giving the presentation?

_____

3 What is the subject?

_____

4 What are the stages of the presentation?

_____

_____

_____

2 `2.19` **Listen to the presentation and tick all the things the presenter does.**

1 Give an example ☐

2 Introduce the subject ☐

3 Finish one subject ☐

4 Analyse a point ☐

5 Refer to a visual aid ☐

6 Summarise and conclude ☐

7 Start another subject ☐

8 Answer a question ☐

3 `2.19` **Reorder the words to make sentences from the presentation. Listen and check.**

1 let me all, first of where the idea you from came tell so.

_____

2 they instance, small umbrellas for have those

_____

3 told about the idea I've so, you

_____

4 illustrate my point, the short film to look at

_____

5 I may later, back that if point to come I'll

_____

6 now the moving to advantages on so,

_____

7 the Carry Chair by saying anyone I'd like perfect for to recap that is

_____

8 my presentation coming you for everyone thank to

_____

WRITING SKILLS:
a tactful business email

4 `2.19` **Listen to the presentation again and make a list of positive and negative points about the presentation and the product. You might want to consider the following issues:**

– content

– organisation

– formality of the presentation

– use of visual aids

– relevance of presentation

– relationship with audience

– responding to questions

POSITIVE	NEGATIVE
Product	Product
Presentation	Presentation

5 **As Evelyn's line manager, write a tactful email telling her why the company cannot produce the product and why her presentation was a failure.**

_____

_____

_____

_____

_____

_____

_____

Science and nature

12.1 SCIENCE FICTION

VOCABULARY: words from the lesson

1 Read the short course descriptions for a university science department and label the subject areas.

1 _____: The scientific study of matter in outer space, especially the positions, dimensions, distribution, motion, composition, energy, and evolution of celestial bodies and phenomena.

2 _____: The science of life and of living organisms, including their structure, function, growth, origin, evolution, and distribution.

Within this subject area, we will particularly look at the area of 3 _____, which deals with animals and animal life, including the study of the structure, physiology, development, and classification of animals.

4 _____:The study of the earth and its features and of the distribution of life on the earth, including human life and the effects of human activity. Within this subject area, we will particularly look at the subject of 5 _____, which is the scientific study of the origin, history, and structure of the earth.

This joint course consists of 6 _____; the science of the composition, structure, properties, and reactions of matter, especially of atomic and molecular systems and 7 _____; the science of matter and energy and of interactions between the two, grouped in traditional fields such as acoustics, optics, mechanics, thermodynamics, and electromagnetism.

2a Reorder the letters to make words connected with the topics from Exercise 1. Do not change the first letter.

1 bsolsmo _blossom_____

2 plinalotnio _____

3 petheylon _____

4 mruyrec _____

5 cavinorsour _____

6 prastiae _____

7 gatenimre _____

8 regdi _____

2b Use the words from Exercise 2a to complete the paragraphs.

1 If seeds were to _____ at the wrong time, for example in winter, they would probably die.

2 Look at the topography of the south, and you can see a narrow _____ extending north from the James River to the Hampshire border.

3 A _____ bag is better than any other material because the amount of energy that goes into their manufacture is minimal.

4 The malaria _____ is one of our most dangerous enemies, evading the immune system and rapidly acquiring resistance to the drugs designed to kill it.

5 Our programme helps to maintain a healthy population of honey bees for the _____ of agricultural and horticultural crops and wild plants, and the production of honey.

6 _____ plants are plants that attract, capture, and digest insects to obtain nutrients such as nitrogen.

7 The mining of _____ has declined in recent decades, as international concern over the health threat to the environment has mounted.

8 During the evolution of flowers, for example, _____ of one type is not directly modified to produce ones of another type.

READING

1 Read the article below quickly and answer the questions.

1 What is the writer trying to do?

   a) To present an argument.

   b) To explain what something is.

   c) To describe a situation.

   d) To compare and contrast two situations.

2 What is the writer's bias?

   a) He/She believes a crisis is coming.

   b) He/She does not believe a crisis is coming.

   c) He/She is not sure.

   d) He/She does not express an opinion one way or another.

PEAK OIL –
Have we consumed our future?

Oil is the fluid foundation of globalized society and has also contributed mightily to the increase of the global population. After the Second World War, the spread of petroleum-derived industrial fertilizers caused agricultural yields to double between 1947 and 1979. The world population **did** the same. Petroleum also serves as the primary feedstock for an array of petrochemicals capable, as the word plastic implies, of assuming almost any shape and consistency: I am writing this on a plastic keyboard and you are reading it on a page printed with plastic-based ink while poor people wearing plastic sandals are elsewhere carrying water in plastic jugs. According to a recent study, economic growth and the increased use of petroleum go hand-in-hand, which naturally leads you to wonder what a peak and decline in petroleum use would do to our habitual prosperity. A frightening theory that started off as the sort of thing people only discussed in the dark corner of the Internet but which is now being discussed in the highest corridors of power suggests that if the availability of fossil fuels, which have done so much to increase the productivity of people and nature alike, were to drop off, we would be facing a Peak Oil Crisis!

In simplest terms, peak oil refers to the moment when global oil output reaches a maximum rate – measured in millions of barrels per day or even billions per year – and then goes into decline. The theory was formulated by the American geophysicist M. King Hubbert, who in 1956 (when he happened to be employed by Shell) made the controversial and, it turned out, correct prediction that US oil production would top out around 1970 and begin falling. Hubbert's **model** proposes that the rate of oil production for a given oil-bearing region – including, ultimately, the region known as the earth – will follow a more or less bell-shaped curve, with the peak of the curve (maximum production) arriving whenever approximately half the recoverable oil has been extracted from the ground.

At first it may seem strange that the rate of oil production should decline before there's hardly any oil left; after all, methods for finding new oil and producing more from existing oil fields do improve over time. There are many misconceptions about peak oil but the most frequent **one** is that the theory is false because we're discovering new oil fields all the time – massive undersea deposits off the coast of Brazil, for example, or once marginal fields in North Dakota now coming into production. But discovering and developing oil fields is a bit like picking up broken glass: You first sweep up the big and easy-to-spot pieces (such as Saudi Arabia's supergiant reservoirs), whereas recovering the smaller splinters (offshore reserves, marginal fields) requires more skill and more time. The easy-to-get oil comes as you climb the slope to the peak; the harder-to-get oil is what you develop as you slide back down. Peak oil is a classic case of increasing effort producing diminishing returns.

The main questions surrounding peak-oil theory concern exactly when we will reach Hubbert's peak and what happens when we **do so**. Hubbert himself, who died in 1989, predicted in the early '70s that the peak of global production would arrive by 2000. While this prediction was obviously incorrect, if **it** landed anywhere within a hundred miles of the truth, as a number of researchers contend, we could be in for some trouble. An absolute decrease in petroleum supplies at a time of rising demand (projected to reach 125 million barrels a day worldwide by 2030) would necessarily thwart much of that demand, and what diminishing supplies remained could be expected to command ever greater prices until some alternative transportation-fuel infrastructure was in place.

Because the replacement of crude oil with some combination of alternatives is at best a project of decades and at worst a pipe dream, it's hard to imagine that the near-term arrival of peak oil wouldn't spell serious difficulties for the world economy. It would possibly spell global recession or, if not, a scenario not too dissimilar to Mad Max 2, with neo – barbarians slaughtering each other over the odd remnant barrel of oil.

2 Read the article on page 82 again and tick (✓) the true statements.

1 The economy grows at a slower speed than the increase in the use of petroleum. ☐

2 Peak Oil theory is no longer considered a conspiracy theory. ☐

3 Peak Oil is defined as the moment when the oil runs out. ☐

4 It is wrong to think that the discovery of new oil will postpone an oil crisis. ☐

5 People on the street are not convinced by the Peak Oil theory. ☐

6 The oil we find in later years is more difficult to get at. ☐

7 Hubbert's prediction of when oil production would peak was mistaken. ☐

8 The world has already developed an alternative resource to oil. ☐

GRAMMAR: substitution and ellipsis

3 What do the bold words in the underlined sentences in the text refer to?

1 _____

2 _____

3 _____

4 _____

5 _____

6 _____

4 Answer the questions.

a) Write one example of ellipsis in the text.

_____

b) Which use of ellipsis or substitution is missing from the text?

_____

5 Rewrite the second sentences from each pair using either substitution or ellipsis.

1 The theory that we will develop a new source is quite likely. That we will end up with no computers or cars is more likely.

_____

2 Cotton has been with us for centuries. Cotton is strong and easy to develop. (Don't use 'it'!)

_____

3 A: Do we know if the crisis has started?
B: I believe that the crisis hasn't started yet.

_____

4 A: They must have driven to work
B: No. It's impossible: They can't have driven to work

_____

5 A: We finally managed to find a set of tools. The set
B: of tools is the best that we could find.

_____

6 A: We have no choice but to close the mine.
B: If you close the mine, hundreds will lose their jobs

_____

7 I asked you to monitor the situation. You failed to monitor the situation.

_____

8 I don't mind which car we buy. However, I think the family car would be better.

_____

LISTENING

6 [2.20] Listen to six people (A–F) giving their opinions on Peak Oil. Match the description of the person with the speaker.

1 An ordinary person from the street ___

2 An engineer at one of the new oil sources. ___

3 A journalist ___

4 The CEO of a petrol company ___

5 A sociologist ___

6 The Leader of the Peak Oil Awareness League ___

VOCABULARY: informal phrases

7 [2.20] Listen again and complete the phrases.

1 So they don't _____ with it.

2 Well I'll tell you I've _____ with the _____!

3 The sooner _____ stop _____, the better.

4 The situation is _____.

5 There's always people _____ this stuff.

6 Whenever doubts are raised about this site, the same argument _____.

DICTATION

1a 2.21 Listen and write what you hear.

_____

_____

_____

_____

_____

_____

1b Read what you have written and replace the word 'group' with a suitable collective noun.

READING

2 Read the article on page 85 and complete the information sheet.

Name of Bug	1 _____
Reason for its return?	2 _____
How does it get in your house?	may get into 3 _____ or 4 _____
Signs of infestation	5 _____ on the body
Protection	Examine 6 _____ day call in 7 _____ when using 8 _____ don't _____ take off 9 _____ when _____
NOTE	Bedbugs will visit your house whether it is 10 _____ or _____.

EXTRA VOCABULARY: words from the text

3 Match the underlined words in the article on page 85 with the following definitions.

1 a strong feeling in society that being in a particular situation or having a particular illness is something to be ashamed of _____

2 a lot of rats, insects, etc. in one place that usually cause damage _____

3 people or animals that are behind the others in a group, because they are moving more slowly _____

4 to become very successful or very strong and healthy _____

5 to get off a ship or aircraft _____

6 to search someone by feeling their body with your hands _____

7 completely got rid of something such as a disease or a social problem _____

8 laziness, untidiness, carelessness _____

9 animals, plants or people on which a smaller animal or plant is living as a parasite _____

10 sleeping _____

GRAMMAR: nominalisation

4 Read the article again and underline the text which the following three nominalised sentences refer to.

A The advice is to not use public transport.

B This skill means they can easily travel with you from one place to another.

C A vast number of returnees from abroad offer bedbugs a huge choice of hosts.

5 Match the uses 1–3 with the examples of nominalisation in Exercise 4.

1 It can be used to summarise a previous point. ____

2 It can combine two clauses so is more economical. ____

3 It can be used to avoid mentioning who does an action. ____

Bedbugs: these tiny pests are back with a vengeance.

Maybe you remember, when you were a kid, your mummy telling you as she turned out the light 'Night night. Sleep tight. Don't let the bedbugs bite'. I used to believe there were millions of these little animals in bed with me. I just couldn't
5   see them. It's of course not true. But it could be. I can't decide where, in our battle with the bedbugs, we started fighting back. Was it when my son's class teacher called my wife to express her concern about the number of bites on his arms, body and face? 'He says they're ... bedbug bites,' she said, disbelievingly. 'That's
10 right,' my wife replied. 'We've got an infestation that we're being treated for.' 'Oh, I understand – I've come across bedbugs, when I've been travelling in Africa.' The words 'but not when I've been teaching in north London' went unspoken.
    Was it when, for four nights running, our eight-year-old
15 daughter kept us awake with her star-shaped sleeping position, because she was too afraid to sleep in her own bed after having awoken to see a pair of bedbugs lazing on her pillow?
    Be warned: we are not unusual. Bedbugs are on their way back, despite having been all but eradicated in the developed world by
20 the 1980s.
    In the US, in the postwar years, DDT was used to kill them off. In this country the authorities shamed the population into seeking their own treatment, by drawing a link between infestation and slovenliness, thus establishing a stigma that survives today.
25 In fact, your cleanliness or otherwise makes no difference to whether bedbugs set up home with you. All they're interested in is your blood. If you encounter them, there's a decent chance they're coming home with you. And you stand a decent chance of encountering them.
30 So why are the bedbugs biting? What brought them back to Britain? The simplest explanation is globalisation. Bedbugs are hugely effective hitchhikers: if you sleep in an infested room, they may climb into your luggage, or into your clothes. When you get home, they disembark and set up home in the
35 darkest corners of your bedroom, coming out in the hours before dawn to suck blood from your slumbering body. With more and more of us travelling abroad to regions where bedbugs were never eradicated, more and more of us are likely to bring them back. They thrive in homes inhabited
40 by large numbers of people, where they are able to feed and breed freely. Many people, it seems, don't react to bites and so don't realise they have a problem until they find a live bug.
    Where did we get our bugs? The exterminator estimated
45 our house had been occupied for five months and reckoned we'd got them from public transport. That, he told us, is where most people pick up bedbugs. It's simple logic really: a vast number of people, including plenty who have returned from abroad use public transport offering bedbugs a huge
50 choice of hosts. But the transport companies are hardly at fault. Do we expect them to frisk every traveller for bedbugs? Could they check every bus and every train every night for bedbugs? That is what it would take to get the transport system clear. In the meantime, David Cain advises
55 commuters: 'Don't sit down on public transport.'
    When the exterminator had treated our kids' rooms, he left us with a lengthy manual of instructions. The kids needed to stay in their rooms because if the bugs' food source was removed, they would just infest new rooms. We were
60 to examine the beds every day for living and dead bugs, and after two weeks we were to 'deep clean' their rooms in the hope of eradicating the last stragglers. That fortnight seemed to last for ever. It was during that time that our son's teacher made the call that shamed us. It was on the last
65 day of the fortnight that I took apart the bunk beds to find them crawling with living bugs. Even after the deep clean – performed by a woman who advised us that, in addition to never sitting down on public transport, we should always
70 remove our clothes before entering a bedroom – we still needed another chemical treatment. That took place last week. We are praying that by next week we are clear – so we can get back to
75 killing the mice.

LISTENING

6   2.22 Listen and match the questions A–E with the answers 1–5 you hear.

A   Why has there been an increase in bedbugs in recent years?

B   What is the history of bedbugs?

C   What do you do if you are infested?

D   How do you know you have got a bedbug infestation?

E   Haven't bed bugs been eradicated?

1   _C_   2 ___   3 ___   4 ___   5 ___

7   2.22 Listen again. Which of the following things DIDN'T the speaker say?

1   Bedbugs don't carry disease. ___

2   Bedbugs move quickly from one room to the next. ___

3   Bedbugs started in the US. ___

4   10 per cent of people have no problems with bedbug bites. ___

5   You can solve the bedbug problem yourself. ___

6   Bedbugs are mentioned in literature. ___

7   Banning chemicals that were dangerous to us helped bedbugs. ___

8   You can find bedbugs on planes. ___

KEY LANGUAGE:
Referring to what other people have said

1 [2.23] Listen to Amira giving a talk on insects and answer the questions.

1 What does the speaker suggest will happen as a result of global warming?

_____

2 What two functions of insects are mentioned?

_____

3 How many years' data did they use?

_____

4 What method to keep insects cooler did not work?

_____

2 Complete Amira's sentences.

A As Amira _____ insects are vital in tropical habitats.

B _____ Amira said _____ this research covering a fifty year-period intrigues me. Why fifty years?

C _____ I understand you _____, Amira, you're _____ that your research is not just relevant to insects?

D _____ I could just _____ on something Amira said about a fitness programme for insects.

E Amira _____ that rain patterns would also be affected, _____ that we could have more drought or rainstorms, I suppose?

F With _____ to Amira's _____ that animals such as penguins are in less danger, I am still not convinced.

G _____ we should _____ to what Amira said, which was this research also has implications for other issues than just that of insects.

3 [2.23] Listen to the lecture again and put the statements (A–G) in the correct order. One statement is not.

1 ___ 2 ___ 3 ___ 4 ___ 5 ___ 6 ___

STUDY SKILLS: examination skills

1 Read the examination tips below and match sentences 1–10 with sentences a–j.

1 Long essay questions can be a challenge. Plan your answer. Spend a few minutes planning at the start.

2 Before the exam, make very, very sure that there are no notes accidentally left in your pocket. It would be a disaster to get caught with notes when you didn't even intend to cheat and just left it there by accident.

3 Quickly scan through the questions on the paper before you start so that your subconscious gets a chance to think a bit before you actually start the question.

4 Memorising things just before the exam is not a good idea, particularly in subjects that emphasise understanding rather than a repetition regurgitation of the facts.

5 With listening papers, don't sit there staring into space while the moderators set up the tape / CD / computer.

6 Arrive on time.

7 Remember to breathe. Get lots of oxygen in.

8 Answer the question that you are being asked.

9 Get to know the exam, before you take the exam. This is what past papers are for ... and teachers, hopefully.

10 If you are taking a foreign language exam, where the grammar part of the paper has a text with spaces you need to fill in, read the text first before you start answering.

a) It's said to improve the ability to concentrate.

b) You are unlikely to remember anything better in five minutes of staring just before an exam begins (although you might remember the odd fact or formula), and it may just increase the panic.

c) Then you know what to expect; and you can find out where your strengths and weaknesses are. It helps with working out timing and strategies, too.

d) This will help you to understand the context and content and make choosing the right answer easier.

e) Know in advance precisely when and where the exam is being held.

f) You can also plan what to say before you go back and attempt the question.

g) You could even memorise an essay you wrote earlier in the year and fit it to a question that is similar.

h) In the UK, they can cancel your entire GCSE results on that, and it could destroy your future.

i) Read the questions thoroughly and think about the information you are going to hear.

j) Writing lots of clever stuff isn't going to do any good if it is irrelevant.

WRITING SKILLS: a personal statement

2 Read the personal statement and tick (✓) the four things wrong with it.

1 It isn't convincing, and suggests the writer isn't committed or enthusiastic. ☐

2 It shows that the writer is only interested in taking what they want for their own ends. ☐

3 There are contradictory pieces of information. ☐

4 There are obvious gaps and important parts of the writer's life are missing. ☐

5 You cannot hear the writer's voice in the statement. It is not personal. ☐

6 Little time or care has been taken over the writing. ☐

7 The language makes the writer sound pretentious or not very intelligent. ☐

8 There isn't a strong conclusion. ☐

3 Rewrite the underlined sections of the personal statement to make it more convincing.

Someone should always take an interest in the human mind and the way it works. I find this quite interesting, too. I studied psychology at school and then continued reading about it in my own time. At university, I hope to find more to interest me in the subject.

I worked with primary children as a classroom assistant in my final year at school. As well as providing practical experience in a primary school, this opportunity also allowed me to develop skills in communication.

Success in my school studies and extra work experience in a drop-in centre for people with mental health problems for three hours every Monday afternoon in my summer holidays, has given me a the experience I need to approach a degree course in psychology with confidence and enthusiasm.

In my summer holidays I had a part time job as a customer service assistant in Tesco. This provided me with an opportunity to work as a team co-operating with others and at the same time learning to be independent. Often I have been able to work on my own initiative, which I have enjoyed immensely as it has allowed me to use my own ideas and thoughts.

Outside of school, I enjoy socialising and meeting new people. I am an honest, reliable and friendly person with very high intelligence. In June I achieved one of my ambitions by passing my driving test at the first attempt.

My experiences during my post-sixteen studies have enabled me to be independent, organised and self-disciplined, which should prove invaluable preparation for life at university. _I understand the importance of studying and hope that studying psychology will motivate me to study hard._

_____

_____

_____

_____

_____

_____

_____

_____

CD1

Lesson 1.1 Track 1.2

1 This was certainly more common in the past than it is today. If you had money then you got a better education. If you didn't have enough money you were lucky if you got an education at all.

2 Only recently have people started considering that we should be teaching children skills that enable them to communicate better and understand each other.

3 The style of teaching at this time treats every student exactly the same. There is a process where the more gifted or clever students are pulled down to the level of the weakest students – the lowest common denominator.

4 The attempt to promote more autonomous learning and study at home makes this issue more common. The truth is that if the teacher isn't watching, some student will abuse the trust and copy other people's work or get someone else to do the work for them.

5 This term probably didn't even exist. Most teachers basically taught what they'd been taught or even according to what they felt most comfortable with. This idea of everyone following the same pattern is quite new, or at least, now more common.

6 At that time, this would mostly be just written papers where students were expected to repeat exactly what they had learnt. Nowadays, some will be spoken and some will even be on computer but a form that involves monitoring progress has become more important than just seeing what someone has achieved by the end of a course.

7 Today we see classes for the same age-group being divided according to ability. Stronger students are put together in the same class and work at a faster pace while students who need more support are given the time to improve.

Lesson 1.2 Track 1.3

A Gosh, I've never thought about it. I've never wanted lots of money or anything like that but I was brought up in a single-parent family, so I think I was always looking for affection and attention. So for me, I suppose I would consider myself successful if there is someone in my life I can be affectionate with.

B To be successful I think the first thing you have to be is ambitious. If you're not prepared to do anything to succeed, you probably won't get there. You don't need to be accomplished in an educational sense. Look at me! I'm well on my way to being a millionaire and I had most of my education on the streets!

C Your true personality actually doesn't matter if you want to be successful because it is really more what people see, not who you are, which will decide whether you are going to be successful or not. Basically you have to be a salesperson, be persuasive. If you can sell oil to Texans then you will probably be a success.

D I think I'm allergic to success. Every time I try something risky it fails. I've started three ventures over the last five years and all of them went bankrupt. I don't know what I'm doing wrong, you know, as I've followed all the advice. I've even been to self-help

groups. I became superstitious at one stage and was convinced that any number 13 in the building would mean my venture was going to fail. Now I believe that all success is really just about dumb luck.

E You have to be passionate about what you do if you want to be successful. You have to live it and breathe it. The problem is then your passion can turn into a drug. That's why rich people keep wanting more. And of course if you let it go on it can destroy your life. You have to be really careful because success can be toxic.

F I suppose many people think success means becoming famous. I mean, I don't think that's the case. I think you are a success if you're just, well, happy with your life. You don't have to be powerful or skilful in anything. I suppose the fact that I have a wife, two children, we are healthy and we have our own house means that I am successful. I certainly feel like that.

Lesson 1.3 Track 1.5

Well I'm pretty confident. I'm definitely planning to enter the job market this year and as I got a first, I'm expecting it to be easy to find a job. I hadn't thought about what job I wanted to do before I chose my university subject and I suppose some people might say that English Language and Literature isn't very useful unless you're planning to enter education. However, I think companies want applicants to have finished university and done well rather than finishing any specific subject. My sister studied archaeology and by the end of this year she will have been working for five very successful years as a Sales Manager at Arkins.

My friends still haven't made a decision as they are waiting to see what the markets will do. My best mate, Raul, had been thinking about taking a year out until he saw the amount of money he had to pay back on his student loan so now he's desperate to find something. Personally, I think the markets have been fluctuating for years but if you've got what people need then you are sure to get the right job. I know there aren't many people out there who've got the background and qualifications that I've got. And I can tell you I'm going to be tough in negotiating my salary. Companies have been fighting for people like me so I won't be considering a starting salary of anything less than £35,000 a year when I start.

All in all I'm pretty confident so postgraduate work just seems to be wasted time when I could be earning big money.

Lesson 1.4 Track 1.6

A: Right, there's a lot of competition for this post so let's make it clear what we are really looking for.

B: Well let me start by saying age is a pre-requisite. They've got to be over 18 and under 30. We can't get visas for anyone under 18 and any older than 30 and I can see insurance issues.

C: Yes. You're absolutely right. I think it's also essential that they are fit. Looking after kids at a summer camp is a pretty strenuous job.

A: Isn't it just! Well, I imagine it would be helpful if they had done some previous work with kids.

C: That's not that easy to find but it would probably give them an edge.

B: What about gender?

A: That's not an issue as there are boys and girls at the camp but they have to have

interpersonal skills. They are going to have to sort out fights between kids, social problems and ...

B: They must have discipline. The kids need discipline.

A: Oh come on!

B: I'm serious! It'd be a good thing if they've been involved in youth groups, like scouts, girl guides, that sort of thing.

C: Hmm, next you'll be saying that it's essential that they can sing round campfires.

B: Well, building campfires and some climbing skills would be an advantage ...

Lesson 2.3 Track 1.8

H: The first person I spoke to was Judy Boyd, UK Director of VSO. I asked her what she thought was going wrong with Volunteer Tourism.

JB: Spending your gap year volunteering overseas is now a rite of passage for young people and the gap year market has grown considerably. However, while there are many good gap year providers, we are concerned about the number of badly planned and unsupported schemes – ultimately benefiting no one apart from the travel companies that organise them. Young people could be better off travelling and experiencing different cultures than signing up to a volunteer scheme that benefits no one, least of all those who are most in need of it.

H: When talking to Robert Hargreaves, Managing Director of Year Out, I found a similar message being sent.

RH: The problem is many volunteers are naïve when picking where to go or who to go with. They don't do enough research, and they think a quick look on the Internet is the way to go about booking. All our members encourage potential volunteers to do their research. They'll put them in contact with recently returned volunteers and encourage parents to get more involved. The problem we face is the sector regenerates itself – every year a new set of clients needs to be educated. And believe me that education is necessary. I mean, you won't believe some of the rubbish that's being done out there. I mean, some projects promoted by unregulated companies are little use to anyone. There's one that does a 'turtle census' in South America which basically counts the same animals each week with no end result. Another one I've heard of was, was where volunteers who signed up for rural conservation work, they had to work as office staff for the company and never actually got to their destination. And these are some of the less worrying examples I've heard of. What causes me most concern is the trend for young, mainly female volunteers to head off independently to Ghana and seek projects once they arrive. The High Commission in Accra told me it's become a real problem – there's a rumour going around the UK that it's easy to get involved once you're there. It shows why people should have some support.

H: Tabitha Graham, Operations Director of Madadventurer thinks that reputable organisations must collaborate with local communities.

TG: We only pick projects where the local people have identified a need. That way volunteers are welcomed by the community and can make a valid contribution. While the cost of booking with established operators is higher than going direct, the benefits of this sort of 'package-style' support is worth paying for. Volunteers also benefit from the strong social responsibility that placement agencies bring.

There really is potential in this market. Two-week packages are available for those who want to fit aid work into a vacation. I've also heard of a company aiming solely for the over-40s – called Gaps for Grumpies. This shows that the industry is making in-roads into the older generation. They have an awareness of global issues and often, because of their careers or life experience, can contribute more than the young. The bottom line is we have already seen that large travel companies are starting to get involved in the sector and I assure you they will continue to do so. But big organisations can only get involved if they stick to basic principles.

Lesson 2.4 Track 1.9
Gavin Glover

G: Good morning everyone and thank you for coming. For those who don't know me, my name is Gavin Glover and I am the Project Manager for the Falmer Community Stadium Project. First of all, I'd like to thank Brighton Council for setting up this meeting and supplying the venue. Right, the issue on the table is clear. Brighton and Hove Albion football club wish to build a new football stadium near the university by the village of Falmer. However, today we need to address the concerns of interested parties and come to a solution that will be acceptable to everyone. Paul Harker is here to represent Brighton and Hove Albion. Steven Baxter is here on behalf of Brighton and Hove Council. Sarah Edge will be representing the National Heritage and Conservation Society and Jane Marks the villagers of Falmer. Let's begin by each person having the chance to outline their positions.

Lesson 2.4 Track 1.10
Part 1
Paul Harker

PH: Brighton and Hove Albion has been under a cloud for many years. Firstly, we had our ground sold by an owner trying to destroy the club. Then for the last seven years we've been renting an athletics stadium which is simply not suitable for professional football. It's an absolute priority for the club that we build ourselves our own stadium. Without it this club has no chance of survival. It simply isn't possible for a club to survive when it's losing the amount of money we are on a weekly basis because we don't have our own stadium.

Part 2
Jane Marks, Gavin

JM: As representative of the villagers of Falmer who are about to have their village destroyed, I'd like to make our position very clear. We don't want the club anywhere near us!

GG: OK, you've been very clear about your opposition to this project, but you haven't really outlined your objections. What exactly do you mean by 'have their village destroyed'?

JM: We all own land and property which we spent good money and time developing. The building of a stadium on our doorstep will result in a massive drop in the value of our holdings. We are all agreed that the idea of a stadium near Falmer is just not negotiable.

GG: Not at all?

JM: No!

Part 3
Steven Baxter

SB: Jane, I understand where you're coming from. The council are deeply concerned that Falmer's inhabitants do not suffer as a result of this proposal. However, a football club and a football stadium is not only good for the prestige of the city, but it also creates jobs and revenue for the city. We should not underestimate the effect of sport tourism on the city and, although Brighton is a tourist resort, there is no question that sport tourism would be a further benefit. We also should not forget the positive effects on the populace of a successful team and now Leopold Bloom, the businessman and millionaire has offered to finance the club provided Falmer gets built. It's vital for the town as a whole to have the stadium built if we want to stay living in a prosperous and successful city.

Part 4
Sarah Edge, Steven

SE: So Steve, if I understand you correctly, what you are saying is that if we don't build the stadium in Falmer, it will be a disaster for the city. Is that right?

SB: Well, maybe it's not THAT dramatic but, in a nutshell, yes.

SE: Everyone seems to forget that Falmer is an officially recognised area of natural beauty …

SB: … which is about to lose its status …

SE: and is therefore protected by the government. In addition, it is home to countless species of wild birds, some of whom are endangered …

SB: I'm sorry but that is just not the case …

SE: Well that's exactly what you would say! It seems to me that you just won't face up to your responsibility to the environment! I mean, think of what you're destroying …

Lesson 3.2 Track 1.12
Greg, Laura

G: So, Laura, who are they key new names of Interpol's most wanted?

L: Well, if you've been watching the news this week, the first name shouldn't be too much of a surprise.

G: Oh, you mean that Chinese guy …

L: Yes, Shin Ju Qui is suspected of heading the largest organisation involved in the illegal production and trafficking of medicinal drugs. The request has of course come from the Chinese government but there are at least eleven countries that would like to get their hands on him.

G: I can believe that. Not a nice man we've heard.

L: That's correct, he is also under suspicion for the murder of at least two former business associates yet it is for the illegal medicine trade that he is included in the list.

G: OK and who's next?

L: Well, it is believed that as a result of Jens Lagerman's activities, two months ago all Danish government websites went down for three hours.

G: Wow! I don't remember hearing that on the news.

L: Well you probably wouldn't. The Danish government have tried to keep it quiet. They're still investigating the possible damage the loss of these websites might mean. Jens is known to be a computer whiz kid and has been a suspect in anti-governmental activity before now.

G: Wasn't he involved in the Smuggler Island illegal downloading?

L: Well, we think he was. However, again, there is probably not enough evidence to put him on the list for that.

G: Next …?

L: Well this one is probably the most controversial. This is a wanted request for an American citizen, Isaac Butler, by the Bhutanese government.

G: What has he done?

L: He is accused of stealing many rare and valuable national artefacts that are the property of the Bhutanese government. What's strange about this is that Isaac is a well-known traveller and writer who has lived in Bhutan for 25 years. Supposedly, he does have such artefacts yet they have been on public display in his house during his time in Bhutan and nothing has been said. He has always said that if Bhutan wanted them they could ask him.

G: So what has he done? Isn't he innocent? Surely the Most Wanted list shouldn't be used in this way.

L: First of all, we don't have all the facts. Secondly, the Interpol's Most Wanted list is not there for us to make judgements about what is right or wrong. It is an information board for our members to make requests. Butler is innocent until proven guilty.

G: Right, well, OK … still smells fishy to me …

Lesson 3.3 Track 1.13
Part 1

Today's lecture will be on the role and activities of diplomatic missions around the world. I'm sure all of you must have seen the siege of the Australian High Commission in London three weeks ago. Many students have come and asked me why Australia has a High Commission and not, for example, an embassy. In this short lecture we will present the different forms of mission and then talk a little about roles.

Part 2

A permanent diplomatic mission is commonly known as an embassy, or occasionally, a chancery. What is the difference? The embassy is the ambassadorial residence, where the ambassador lives and this is usually where all the ambassadorial work is done. But for example, Mr Albert Jones, who left the US embassy in Russia last year, needn't have lived where all the work was done – that place is called the chancery – he could have lived in the separate ambassadorial residence, called Spaso House. Of course, as we know from his visit last month, Mr Jones slept on the sofa in his office most of the time! So, although the chancery and the embassy are often the same place, they don't always have to be.

Part 3

During the first few years, after the French revolution, the French government ought to have had a French embassy in London. It didn't. Rather it had a legation. This is a diplomatic mission headed by a lower-ranking official. This was because neither country considered the other important enough. England regarded the French government as illegal and the French thought the British government were immoral and their natural enemy. Today, in this world of political correctness, legations have become obsolete. However, one area of distinction remains. Instead of embassies, countries that still belong to or are associated with the British Commonwealth, such as Australia, have High Commissions instead of Embassies. This could have been changed to represent the changes in the political state but is a mark of respect to the existence of one King or, as we have today, Queen of all these states.

Part 4

Has anyone seen the film *The Killing Fields*? Well you needn't have seen it to know that it is a commonly held belief that once you are on the land of the mission, you are in fact in that country and therefore safe from danger. Certainly the Cambodian refugees felt like this when they climbed the walls of the US Embassy. This is called sanctuary. In fact, though, this is not completely true. Sanctuary can happen for a limited time but it is by no means sure or permanent. It is true that a host country cannot enter the grounds of a diplomatic mission without permission but it is very rare that an embassy will act against the wishes of the host country.

Lesson 3.4 Track 1.14

A: Well, thank you for the free and frank discussion, Mr Ambassador. Let's go over the main points again. The islands have been used for the last ten years as a way for terrorists to smuggle arms and money into our country. Our main objective is to remove the threat from these islands to the mainland.

B: Hm-hm.

A: Albertville is the only major town and so the taking of this town should be a key objective.

B: So, if I understand you correctly, you are planning a military action, yes?

A: That is correct, Mr Ambassador.

B: Well, I hope you remember that my country still insists that these islands are part of our national homeland. It would be advisable for you to consider the possible results of such an action. I can assure you my countrymen will not be best pleased.

A: So you will oppose our efforts?!

B: No, I am not saying that. Your priority is to capture these terrorists and remove their threat. It's not, as I understand it, the capture of the island. However, it will be seen as a direct attack on our country.

A: That's just not acceptable, Mr Ambassador.

B: Please calm down Minister! You are aware of the relations between our countries, I take it? One of my main goals as Ambassador to your country is to improve and maintain relations between us, relations that have, let's be honest, not been at their best in recent years. I urge you to reconsider this action and find a solution that does not involve …

A: Mr Ambassador. It is essential to remove these terrorists from our border as quickly as possible. This is not an attack on your country. I think you ought to understand that these terrorists can be just as much a threat to your country as they are to ours.

B: Yes, I can see that.

A: So we are not just doing it for ourselves. We also aim to relieve the tension of the whole region through this action. And it will be our soldiers taking the risk!

B: Yes, it will be your soldiers taking the risk, but it will be our citizens who will be in the firing line. I strongly recommend that you do not forget the danger to our people by YOUR action. Not that of the terrorists.

A: Ah!

B: However, we DO support your attempt to control the terrorist situation and to that end I strongly advise you to consider other options. I can assure you, our government will support any action that does not threaten our territory.

Lesson 4.2 Track 1.15
Gary, Conrad, Reggie

G: Right, we're back on 'Tough Talking' with Gary Nicklin and we're discussing, private health or national health. We're listening to Reggie Perrin and Conrad Grey, Conrad, what do you think?

C: I have only one word for national health and that is 'stupid'! What is it with us? Every country in the world that has a national health service can't stop complaining about it! First of all, you've got to wait months, sometimes years because the waiting lists for even the simplest operation are so long! Half of the hospitals have outdated equipment, some even more than fifty years old and how many stories have we seen in the papers about people dying from post-operative infections? Why? Because the hospitals don't have enough money to keep themselves clean! Come on, people, it's run by the government so of course there's going to be a lack of funding!

R: You really have no idea have you …

C: Me? Get real Reggie! Government spends huge amounts of money on national health.

R: And yet it is under-funded …

C: That means less money on education, less money on … on protecting the country.

R: So killing people is better than saving them …

C: … and what are we paying for? Yes, we! Because it's our taxes that pay for national health. Now, that means I have to pay for drunk drivers who crash their cars into trees. I have to pay for people who smoke themselves to death or … or eat too much. I mean, why should I?

R: Because you don't live on your own, Conrad. Private health companies avoid major surgery as much as they can because the costs can never be covered by the patient. Secondly, anyone who has a condition is then charged extra by the private insurance companies. The people who actually need health support are being asked to pay more!

C: Because they are the ones who are ill! Why should the healthy pay?

R: Well Conrad I hope you never get ill!

C: And I hope you never get treated in a government hospital! I mean, you talk about operations not being done in the private health sector. But look at the National Health Service. Does it look beyond conventional medicine? No! It hides behind its government contracts and tells everyone that alternative medicine doesn't exist!

R: Well, that shows how often you've been into a government hospital. Hypnosis and acupuncture are now common treatments …

C: Well, glad they've seen the light …

R: In fact, it is only the National Health Services who consider preventative medicine! In the private sector, if there is nothing wrong with you yet, then there's nothing to pay for! And let's look at the quality of some of your precious private institutions. There is no organisation in the private sector responsible for checking every private institution. In many places people are not being treated at all.

C: Er, that is where you're wrong. It'll sort itself out. Once it's known a company is not doing a job people won't go there and the institution will lose its customers. The law of supply and demand will force it to improve its quality.

R: And there we see the truth, money being more important than health!

G: And at this point I think we'll take a break!

Lesson 4.3 Track 1.17
Gerard, Penny, Rory

G: So what's the position now?

P: We have now received permission from the government to enter the earthquake zone so our first team is due to arrive in the next three or four hours.

R: Who have we got on the team, Penny?

P: Robert Sikorski is leading the team. They'll go in, assess the situation and then give us a clear indication of what teams we need to send in. I should say, however, that the summary is bound to be pretty horrific. The media is talking of at least twenty thousand dead and are not sure if there won't be more earthquakes.

G: Right. What else Penny?

P: Nana Kouros is about to have a meeting with the supplies team. They'll be contacting all the drugs companies and stocking up on all we need.

G: OK but I won't be pushed around by them. Our role is not to be compromised by the drugs companies.

R: We don't have much to negotiate with, Gerard.

G: Yes we do, Rory. Some of these companies have not been seen in this region and this is likely to increase their exposure in the region.

R: Well, OK. What are the initial estimates of the numbers we will need?

G: Penny's team are about to complete the estimates but I reckon we are looking at … at least 200 people.

P: This is going to be a big one, isn't it?

G: Yes and we need to move fast if we are going to be any use at all.

Lesson 4.4 Track 1.18
Tony, Jill, Sarah, Peter

T: So, we are all agreed, the Natural Health Centre needs a makeover. Jill, What do we need to do to make this place survive?

J: Well, I think the main reason we are struggling is that we haven't been able to get rid of the Natural health stigma.

T: What do you mean by that?

J: We are still offering the fringe services. Tanning salons, acupuncture, natural oils etc.

This means that we are not being accepted as a serious health centre.

S: I think we should actually expand those areas.

T: OK Sarah, let's hear what you have to say.

S: While I accept that promoting these services would be promoting the alternative therapy and beauty therapy side of the centre, it would also be recognising where the money is. After all, we are a private institution and we need the money.

T: I have to say the fact that more than half the visitors use this part of our services means that Sarah is fully justified in her opinions.

J: I don't think anyone can argue with that but that was not our purpose when we opened this place. If we do what Sarah is suggesting, people will inevitably forget that we are trying to be a serious health provider and all that money invested in the maternity wards and the heart clinic will have been wasted. I think we would be better off getting rid of the 'Natural' title in our name if we go that way and that's exactly the kind of thing that we hoped to avoid!

S: Why? We've always argued that alternative therapy needs to be accepted into the mainstream. So, surely you can see that using the label 'Natural' is counter-productive, can't you? If you remove the name then you are saying that these therapies are no longer 'alternative'.

T: That's quite a convincing argument. You may well ask why I have asked Peter Jones to sit in today. As one of our customers I thought he'd give us an insight. What do you think Peter?

P: Well, I'm not sure if anyone is really dealing with the issue. By this, I mean that the Health Centre is not going to fail because of the word 'natural' or because you have acupuncture. It's going to fail if it is not competing in terms of quality. Keep to your original plan. You've only been going a year and people are still getting to hear about you. If I were you I'd promote all the success stories as much I could and get the word out there that you are a success. Look at me! I keep coming back.

T: Thank you, Peter. And I have to say I agree with him. One reason I favour sticking to our original plan is that this is why we started the whole project in the first place. Secondly, I do believe that time will prove us right. Now, let's stop panicking and let's start thinking about how we can market ourselves better.

Lesson 5.2 Track 1.19

And what news is this? Milan has ended New York's five-year reign as the world's top fashion city! The time-consuming task of compiling the list of top fashion capitals was completed by the Global Language Monitor, a U.S. based non-profit group that tracks the frequency of words and phrases in the media, on the Internet and throughout the blogosphere. They announced their results at a breakfast party this morning, in London, which, by the way, I was invited to!

As we all know, the world of fashion is dominated by five cities – New York, Rome, Paris, Milan and London – New York had led the list for five consecutive years. But this year Milan has stolen the crown followed by New York, Paris, Rome and London. Other big movers included Hong Kong and Sao Paulo, which broke into the top ten, while Barcelona and Miami surged.

In Asia, Mumbai outdistanced Delhi. In Australia, Sydney outpaced Melbourne.

There's no doubt that the global economic situation has affected the fashion industry just as it has touched everything else. Thank goodness we are not yet back in the age of hand-made dresses. The fashion shows are still crowded though with fewer bright lights and a little less glamour.

At the unveiling of the list this morning, many were asking why Milan has outperformed New York and its other competitors. The answer is simple. It's Prada, ladies!

Lesson 5.3 Track 21

Raymond Heinze

I start work before I get to the office – basically watching breakfast TV news, listening to the radio and reading magazines and papers on the way in looking for news leads and inspiration. Then I get in and deal with the admin – opening post, replying to emails. I get about 30 emails a day and after filtering out the spam it usually takes me half an hour to deal with them.

I might write a feature or edit one written by someone else and then, as the day progresses I edit news stories as they are written. It's a real team effort here and despite the pressure of publishing on average ten news stories a day, we all have a fantastic time doing the work.

This afternoon, I'll be going to see a press open day, checking out new ranges and new designers. We are constantly looking for new designers and ranges and trends to write about and we also have a shop so part of my day involves liaising with our shop manager.

Most days there is some work out of the office. Later in the afternoon the pressure is on to get the site updated as much as possible before the close of play.

Helen Mumtaz

You won't believe how little of my workload in a day is actual designing! I start off by analysing my business diary for the current day, if I have not got to be out, I set my mind on planned work: graphics, fashions, cup of coffee, a survey of yesterday results. Then it's computer work: reading and answering emails, Internet surfing, scanning images. I'll then work with my webmaster, discussing website development. At some time I need to meet my customers, the contractors and the specialists. I'll need to find time for searching for new ideas by drawing sketches. Then there is the commercial side, fittings and fashion manufacturing that needs to be checked, a bit of research for looking through the fashion-related magazines and studying the local market and also the massive number of phone calls I have to make and take. It's a wonder I find time to sleep!

Luca Canegallo

Having already thoroughly researched the seasonal trends (styles, fabric, colour, etc.) rough sketches of clothing are created. On average this entails upwards of 500 designs per day. This is not a one-day process, but one that can continue for one to two months.

After close reviewing and consultation, specific designs are selected for the collection. Design sketches are created for these selected designs. Pre-costing of the selected designs takes place. Next, flat patterns are created. Then sample garments are produced. When the items are returned from the factory they are inspected and a final costing is conducted. People think there isn't much to the job, after all it's just suits, jeans and t-shirts, isn't it? How wrong they are! The most difficult part of the job is always being creative. Anyone can design a shirt. It has a front, a back, two sleeves and buttons down the front. The challenge is to add that creative detail that gives it 'personality'!

Lesson 5.4 Track 1.22

Paul, Amanada

P: Paul Kelly, can I help you?

A: Hello Paul, it's Amanda from Bellyfirst Fashion House. How are you today?

P: Fine thanks. How can I help you?

A: We want you to organise our show this year. However, preferably with none of the glitches and the cost of last year.

P: Well, we'll see what we can do. When are you planning the event?

A: We want the second week in June.

P: I'm not sure how feasible that would be. That's the height of the fashion season and you won't get the exposure you want. I assume you want the journalists to come?

A: Of course!

P: I was wondering if we might move to the end of May. Then, you'd be ahead of the season. Leave it till later and you risk being compared to other new designs. If you get in first there'd be a chance to surprise the fashion world.

A: Hmm, okay, I'll speak to Reynard and see what he thinks. It'd mean that we'd have to speed up our schedule which might not be feasible. Can we turn to the venue? What about the Langer Centre?

P: Fully booked up, I'm afraid. You need to get in earlier. If we were to reserve the new show area at the Rexon Park, we'd probably get a good deal.

A: The Rexon Park! Oh no, I don't think so. It's a leisure park for heaven's sake. Surely it'd be better to book somewhere with a bit more glamour … panache!

P: The Rexon Park show area is one of the best in the country. Admittedly, that'd mean that you are close to the tourists at the leisure centre but you won't find anywhere better. And suppose you did get some tourists coming in, wouldn't that be good to promote your summer range?

A: Mr Kelly. You have no idea about haute couture do you?

P: Oh come on! It's a fashion show for swimwear isn't it?!

Lesson 6.2 Track 1.23

You've just read about two ideas published three years ago as the ideas that will change the word. Now, I'm going to give you the outline for another three published at the same time. Your task is to research these and find out what's happened to them since they were made public. Have they moved forward or have they disappeared? And what were identified as the reasons why they were successes or failures? Be prepared to present your findings at next week's seminar. OK?

Right let's start with Psiphon. Psiphon is a software programme that was being developed by the University of Toronto's Citizen's lab. At a time when Internet censorship was becoming more of an issue, this simple programme would allow users anywhere to open sites and make transactions without fear of being blocked, provided they followed the rules of the programme. Now, what made this programme so much better than the already existing bypass filters is that it had built-in programmes to avoid being blocked by censors. Of course there are ethical issues with this and it would be interesting to see if the creators of Psiphon have been able to deal with them.

Secondly, the pollution magnet. An object so simple it's actually amazing that no one had come up with it before. As you may know, arsenic is a very dangerous poison that commonly gets into the water supply because of poor pipes or from factories. Arsenic is a major cause of cancer. Vicki Colvin, a professor of chemistry, believed she had found the answer. Using a simple magnet covered with rust particles, she was able to pull the arsenic out of contaminated water. Although this is not a large-scale answer she felt it was the first step to improving the quality of water. Mechanical engineer Hod Lipson felt he had found the answer to make machines that can fix themselves. His prototype? A four-legged robot that looks a bit like a starfish. This robot is able to consider its environment and then change its structure to fit its need. It can therefore change its shape to any circumstance. It's also able to do things like replace a leg if one falls off. This is a first step to, for example, buildings that can repair themselves, airplanes that anticipate mechanical problems, and bridges that can respond to different weights and weather. It could also mean we can develop robots that can be used to explore planets, far from human engineers.

Lesson 6.3 Track 1.24

Good afternoon everyone. First, I should apologise. I had the organisers re-arrange this plenary so that I could open as I feel I have something to say that should affect everything discussed and presented over the next few days. Let me explain by getting straight to the heart of the matter.

From the moment I became involved in the creation of new technologies, I have had my fears of the ethical dimensions challenged. Yet, it was only in the autumn of 1998 that I became anxiously aware of how great are the dangers facing us in the 21st century. I can date the onset of my unease to the day I met Ray Kurzweil, the deservedly famous inventor of the first reading machine for the blind and many other amazing things.

Ray and I were both speakers at a conference, and I met him by chance in the bar of the hotel after both our sessions were over. Ray was sitting with John Searle, a Berkeley philosopher. While they were talking, Ray started a new topic. The subject they started discussing made me take note immediately.

Now, I had missed Ray's talk and the panel that Ray and John had been on, and they now continued the topic of that panel, with Ray saying that the rate of improvement of technology was going to accelerate and that we were going to become robots or part-robots or something like that, and John responded that this couldn't happen, because the robots couldn't be conscious, that is to say, couldn't think for themselves, have feelings, have a soul.

Now while I had heard such talk before, I had always felt that thinking or sentient robots were just science fiction. But now, from someone I respected, I was hearing a strong argument that they were a possibility, not in a hundred years but actually just around the corner. Now I was shocked, especially given Ray's ability to imagine and create the future. I already knew that new technologies like genetic engineering and nanotechnology were giving us the power to remake the world, but a realistic and imminent scenario for intelligent robots surprised me.

It's easy to forget the importance of such breakthroughs. We hear in the news almost every day about some kind of technological or scientific advance. Yet this was no ordinary prediction. In the hotel bar, Ray let me have an early copy of his book *The Age of Spiritual Machines*, which outlined a utopia he predicted – one in which humans gained near immortality by becoming one with robotic technology. On reading it, my sense of unease only grew; I felt sure he had to be understating the dangers, understating the probability of a bad outcome along this path.

With Ray's kind permission I have been allowed to reproduce the handouts in front of you. On them, you will see a passage from his book, which I find most troubling. Please spend a few minutes reading it and then ...

Lesson 6.4 Track 1.25

Maria Perry, Alex Brown

MP: My name is Maria Perry and I would like to present to you Teleblok. Let me start by giving you an amazing statistic. Did you know that every day more than 50,000 calls are made by telemarketing companies, sales companies etc? I'm sure you would agree that these are the type of calls that nobody really wants to answer.

Well, with Teleblok you never need to worry again. It's incredible what this little thing can do. Attach it to your telephone and you will never have to answer annoying calls again. What happens is that when you have a call, this machine answers the call and then asks the caller to identify themselves. The machine then calls you and asks you if you want to access the call. If you do not, then the caller is told that the call is being stopped and then the machine will block all future calls from this person unless you tell them otherwise. At the moment, telephone companies offer two services for blocking calls, neither of which are particularly effective. The best they can offer is to block up to 100 numbers. Teleblok can block up to 5000. I'm sure you would agree that Teleblok is an extraordinarily versatile piece of equipment. Thank you and I'm ready for your questions.

AB: Thank you Maria. Can I ask you how much you plan to sell this for?

MP: The retail price would be 97 pounds.

AB: And how much on average does a telephone cost?

MP: Between 50 and 70 pounds.

AB: Well there is my problem. Why would anyone want to spend more than the cost of a phone to block annoying calls?

MP: It's true that this seems at first glance, quite an expensive piece of equipment. However, let me give you an example. If this machine, at a later date, could be sold as part of the telephone, how much value would it have then? And if we can put it into the telephone, we can also put it into mobile phones.

AB: Now we're talking ...

MP: And I'd just like to give you one other striking example. Do you know how many people use the service already offered? The total number is over a million, yes, one million. They pay three to four pounds a month for this service, which is around 40 pounds a year, whereas with Teleblok they pay one payment of 97 pounds for a

superior service. I think the facts speak for themselves, don't they?

AB: Well, I'm not sure you've got the name right!

MP: Well I accept that I might need some help with naming the product, yes.

AB: Right, Maria, let me tell you where I am ...

CD2

Lesson 7.3 Track 2.3

A: Well, I'd go for farming. If farming didn't exist, then neither would development. Agriculture allowed hunter-gatherer societies to form permanent dwellings. As food was no longer the sole motivation for existence, people could spend time thinking about government, trading and individual specialisation.

B: Well, where would we be without knowing about the unconscious? If you open any book, comic or watch any film in popular culture, you find the unconscious. Only then can we understand about men and women and their relationships to each other.

C: I sometimes think I could do without mine! Albert Einstein's $E=mc^2$ is probably the world's most famous equation. The theory has had an enormous impact on society. If it hadn't been discovered, we wouldn't have nuclear power, which, although controversial, has relaxed our reliance on non-renewable energy like coal and oil. Atom bombs aside, it has also had huge applications for the military – like the synchronization of GPS. Thanks to Einstein we can find anyone anywhere.

D: True, but some people might argue that we could have done without some of those things. I'm not sure about the World Wide Web, either. Only time will tell if this really will have a major impact on society. However I'm sure about soap! It's difficult to imagine, or for that matter, smell, a society without it. It's been with us in any real sense since the mid-19th century when Ignaz Semmelweis, a sharp Hungarian doctor working in Vienna, noticed babies died more often after they were delivered by medical students rather than midwives. He realised medical students had to work on dead people sometimes just before dealing with the living. So, of course, their hands were full of microbes. He introduced a regime of hand-washing and infant deaths dropped substantially making clear the benefits of hand-washing. So you see soap has saved millions of lives.

E: Soap! Really! What about zero? If we don't have zero we don't have mathematics. No algebra, no rocket science. No computers! Everything ends up by coming back to zero. Can you imagine a world without numbers?

F: Yes, I can. If numbers hadn't come along we wouldn't have had money, economics and all of that. Personally, I have to thank people like Fleming who took bacteria and used it to save people. Look at me. I'm 72 years old. If vaccines hadn't been invented, I probably would have died years ago. Can't think of anything more important, myself.

Lesson 7.5 Track 2.4

Do you miss class? Do you, when you actually go to class, ever sit there wishing the professor would just cancel class? When you actually don't mind being in class, do you wish your professor would not give homework? Do you complain when your professors grade too hard? Do you argue the grading of your professor? Do you complain when you have multiple exams on a single day? Is a quality education not important to you?

If you answered "yes" to any of these questions, you are part of the reason why the quality of education has decreased. Students just don't want a challenge or to do any work, at least any more than the bare minimum, to receive an average or high grade.

In every class I hear students complaining about the difficulty of exams or projects. Students are always complaining about going to class, especially when they actually go to them. When a professor gives homework, no one comes prepared to class. We sit there looking shocked and completely offended that he or she would dare give us so many pages to read.

So why do we spend so much money to care so little? In fact, we aren't just apathetic; we are actually annoyed and angry when we have to do work. We are here to get a quality education and the professors are giving in to the students' constant complaints. If enough students complain about a date or a grade, the professor changes it to fit what we want. In that case, why don't they just give us the degrees so we can start doing the jobs we want to do!

Hold on! Why do students make themselves stupid? They need to be challenged in order to be ready to do the jobs they are preparing for correctly and efficiently. Our society is going to be rotten and full of negligent and lazy workers unless we make a change in our attitudes toward the basics: education.

University isn't supposed to be easy and all about drinking and partying or even just being lazy and staying out late. It is about growing up and gaining responsibility, and developing yourself into a well-rounded individual by challenging yourself to a quality education. Fun, extra-curricular and many other miscellaneous activities are, of course, important to our lives, but should not take over why we are here. There are, however, some excellent professors at university who care very much for the education students receive and are not affected by students. There are also some students who take their education very seriously. I hope these select individuals stay strong to their belief in quality education. The bare truth is that lazy students are able to pressure professors and as this happens more and more the quality of students leaving university falls, meaning the capability of people being able to do their jobs properly falls. The inevitable result of this is a country of fools, a failed economy and the laughing stock of the world. Is that what we want? I don't think so!

We should want to be people who truly make a difference in the world after we receive our degrees, not worthless students with worthless degrees.

Lesson 8.2 Track 2.6

Joanne, Presenter

P: And welcome back, we've got Joanne Tatchell, Sales and Marketing manager of Sunshine's Supermarket. Hi Joanne.

J: Hi Jack …

P: Er, it's John … so, Joanne tell us about the new campaign you've got. The three star campaign …

J: Well, um, I'm glad you asked me about that John … John, yes. We at Sunshine believe in balancing the quality with cost … er … while

not losing sight of the needs of our valued customers.

P: Which means that the 3 star cheap versions are for those people who have less money and don't care what they eat?

J: Well, no, no, no not at all, no. Our research shows us that Sunshine customers come from all walks of life and we believe it is just as important to provide for those who are looking for gourmet meals, as well as those who have many young mouths to feed.

P: Well OK, let's look at a tin of baked beans. Your new one star beans cost 50 pence. Your two-star beans cost 40 pence and your three star beans cost 15 pence. So what is the difference between the beans?

J: Well. They're priced according to the needs and financial resources of the customer.

P: Does that mean that they are the same quality but just more expensive for people with more money?

J: No, no, no. Listen John, you used to work in a supermarket …

P: Yes, I …

J: Yes, well everyone knows you get what you pay for and we make sure everyone can get the beans they want.

P: So you are saying that the cheap beans are rubbish. Well they'd have to be at that price!

J: Listen, John, could we have that off the record …

P: I'm afraid I can't do it …

J: Well er … how about editing it out …?

P: We're live Joanne! So, what would you say, then to people saying that it is your low quality products that are responsible for the health problems …

Lesson 8.3 Track 2.7

A: OK, so this is confidential, right?

B: Yes, yes, it is. Ask me anything and it stays in this room.

A: Well, OK. I want to know what my rights are in terms of using social networking sites at work. Can my boss stop us using Facebook at work?

B: Yes. They're well within their rights to prevent you using their equipment and connectivity for personal use, be it personal email and online shopping, or using social networking sites. Though in this company we are happy for you to use it in your breaks during the working day. It would also probably be advisable to use a private e-mail address on Facebook. Unless you are using Facebook officially as part of your job, that is.

A: Oh, OK. Well, can my boss discipline me for using social networking sites during work-time?

B: Yes, quite possibly. When you're at work, you're supposed to be working, so using online social networking on your employers' time could be grounds for a disciplinary process. We do have a policy on personal use of IT equipment, and that makes it clear to you what you are allowed to do, and what you can expect to get in trouble for.

A: Right. Thank you. Can my employer monitor what I'm writing on Facebook whilst I'm at work?

B: Yes and no. We are allowed to monitor what happens at work, including use of the Internet. We can do this with or without your consent, but only if we tell staff clearly in advance what is being monitored. You can

keep a close eye on what we are monitoring on the company IT webpage.

A: Right. I'd better have a look at that. Mm. Can an employer refuse to appoint me to a job because of my Facebook profile?

B: If they haven't yet offered you a job, then an employer is within their rights to consider information from your Facebook profile when making a decision, though it will probably get the company a bad reputation if people found out they were doing this. If you are applying for another post in your company and feel this is happening, just let us know and we'll check it.

Employers are not allowed to discriminate against you in terms of age, gender, sexuality, ethnicity, disability, religion or belief, all of which they could potentially find out if you or your friends discuss it online. Making a case against an employer for this is very hard though, as you need to prove their decision was based on discrimination rather than you not being the best person for the job. However, keep an open mind on this as it is very rare.

A: Yes, well, alright. Finally, er, Should I accept a Facebook friend request from my boss?

B: Well if you want to keep in with your boss then it's probably a good idea. Really it's up to you, isn't it? After all, would you spend time with your boss in your free time? If you would then why not have them as a Facebook friend. Er, there isn't something going on with you and Alyson is there?

A: What? what? er, no, of course not! Well, not yet.

Lesson 9.2 Track 2.8
Part 1

Smacking, or, hitting a child, was a common method of punishment for thousands of years, it seems. Even today, some parents believe that smacking worked for them when they were little, so it should work for their children, too. But, psychologists disagree with parents who think that smacking is a good punishment. The best response to this belief can be seen through a close study of the different types of rewards and punishments that can be given. Let's start, though, by dealing with different kinds of rewards and punishments because smacking is not the only answer.

You can reward and punish, by using either positive or negative approaches. Let's begin with rewards, which psychologists more frequently call "reinforcement". Reinforcement is promoting the repetition of a desired behaviour. We do this typically with positive rewards. Um, a few examples of that would be, for example, when people do a good job, we give people money to reward them. Another good example of positive reinforcement is your monthly or weekly pay slip.

Now, negative reinforcement has the same goal although it is still reinforcement. The word 'negative' however refers to the fact that we're going to take away something that is unpleasant. Um, nagging, in other words, complaining constantly, is a kind of negative reinforcement, which sometimes husbands or wives do, or parents do. They nag their children to clean their rooms. That's not really a punishment. The promise here is that nagging will stop if the husband, wife or child does what is requested.

Here is another example – why do you take aspirin? Do you take it because it tastes good?

I doubt it. You take it because it gets rid of something unpleasant – in this case, of course, the headache.

So, let's now move on to punishments. There are positive and negative punishments.

So, a positive punishment is when you are doing something negative in order to reduce unwanted behaviour. So, examples? Of course, the most common example is smacking. We also shout at children. And, we send people to jail. These are positive punishments. Strange terminology, I know, but that's what they are called.

Lesson 9.2 Track 2.9
Part 2

So, what about smacking? Why is it becoming less and less common? Probably the first reason why people don't smack is because research results show that smacking cannot teach children not to hurt people. Research suggests that despite parents smacking children to stop them hurting other children, it actually, unsurprisingly, sends them the message that it is OK to hurt someone. Secondly, punishment tries to stop the unwanted behaviour while the punisher is there. That is to say, you can only smack someone if you are physically present when the unwanted action takes place. If the punisher isn't there, the method of smacking is ineffective. If the punisher goes to work, for example, the child will probably choose to continue the undesired behaviour. After all, if the punisher isn't there, they can't smack the child.

An alternative to smacking would be 'time-out'. Time-out is a kind of negative punishment. The goal is the same – to get your child to stop doing something unwanted. The punishment is to take your child away from something that makes him or her happy. For example, taking your child away from a game with friends is a kind of negative punishment. The big advantage is that even though it is a kind of punishment, it is a superior alternative to smacking because it is not only a punishment but it also teaches a lesson. For example, if you throw your toys, then Mummy will take you to a room with no toys and you won't have anything to play with.

So, smacking a child is not necessarily a good way to discipline a child. On the contrary, it can produce more unwanted behaviour. And, there really are other and more effective ways to discipline your child, which do not involve physical force.

Lesson 10.2 Track 2.12

Born in the American state of Oklahoma in 1912, Woody Guthrie not only came to represent the suffering of the Dust Bowl years but was an inspiration for just about every successful musician who followed him.

Living his early years in a farming town in Oklahoma, Guthrie was able to experience the lives of those who would later suffer the Dust Bowl. When Woody was young, his mother sang him songs she had learned as a girl. Typical of the farming communities of those times, these songs told stories not only about love but also death and the difficulties of living so close to the land. The hardness of life was distinctly demonstrated to Woody at an early age when his sister died in an accident. The accident happened because Woody's mother had contracted Huntingdon's disease and she gradually lost control over her actions and her speech.

To escape the difficulties of his family life, Woody turned to music. The first instrument Woody learned to play was the harmonica. He also learned how to play the guitar by watching his uncle play. Finding communication with others difficult, Woody preferred to communicate through his music.

As the 1930s began, the United Stated entered the great Depression with many people losing their jobs. To make matters worse for the farming community, the lack of rain at this time heralded the Dust Bowl period.

Like many other people, Woody Guthrie left home to travel around Texas and the south-west looking for work. He often made trips by train. Because he had no money, he would jump on the train's boxcars and ride for free. This was often dangerous, because guards on the train would throw the men off or arrest them. However, Woody found this life exciting. One of the first songs he wrote was about leaving home and fleeing the Dust Bowl.

What affected him most was the suffering he saw. He said: 'When I saw hard-working people suffering under debts, sickness and worries, I knew there was plenty to make up songs about.'

It wasn't long before Woody was playing his songs on the radio. His best known songs were about the troubles people faced during the Depression. In 1938, Woody Guthrie left the radio station where he was working to travel around California. He found that conditions had become worse for many people who had lost their land and fled the Dust Bowl.

Most of these 'Dust Bowl refugees' could only find seasonal farm work like gathering fruit from trees. Farm owners underpaid these workers and they were forced to live in camps that were dirty and had no running water. Hunger and sickness were widespread. The people in the camps seemed to have lost all hope of improving their lives. Woody wrote a song about them called *Dust Bowl Refugees*. The situation infuriated him. He began helping labour organisers establish unions to help the workers. It was during this time that he wrote the song that has now become the second national anthem in America, *This Land is Your Land*. Woody died young but his voice represented the voices of the millions who suffered during the Great Depression. Known as *The Dust Bowl Troubadour*, his legacy still lives on in the works of diverse singers and groups such as Bob Dylan, Bruce Springsteen, U2 and Bon Jovi.

Lesson 10.3 Track 13

Presenter, Dr Barnard, Dr Mancini, Dr Cherkov, Erica Winters

P: So, let's get the ball rolling but starting with the initial question 'Are video games a bad thing?' Dr Barnard?

B: Well, recent research suggests that the traditional opinion in this matter is under attack. Children who spend hours every day playing computer games, on or off the Internet, may not be rotting their brains, as many parents fear. A recent report from the European parliament concluded that computer games are good for children and teach them essential life skills. It's true that many games have a violent reputation but in fact there is no firm proof that playing them has an automatic negative impact on children's behaviour, for example by causing aggression.

M: Yeah, that's correct.

B: In fact, the report suggested that video games can stimulate learning facts and skills such as strategic thinking, creativity, cooperation and innovative thinking, which are important skills in the information society.

P: Dr Mancini?

M: Er, well, um … now I believe that video games are, in most cases, not dangerous. Over the years, we have heard er … evidence from experts on computer games and psychologists from all over the world tell us that video games have a positive contribution to make to the education of minors. I believe that schools should er … consider using games for educational purposes and inform children and parents about the benefits and disadvantages that these games can have.

C: No. Informing children and parents about the benefits and disadvantages does not address the issue. I mean, it's simply ridiculous! You know, what we need is tougher regulation on these computer games, some of which have influenced violent crime among children. You know, let's not forget that! Like the mother of Stefan Pakeerah, a 14-year-old boy from Leicester who was murdered by a 17-year old wielding a knife and hammer who claimed her son's killer was influenced by the computer game Manhunt in which players earn points for killings!

B: Well, the European parliament has conceded that violence in video games can in certain situations stimulate violent behaviour, but there is no need for Europe-wide legislation.

P: What do you suggest?

C: Well perhaps something like preventing the sale to children of games intended for adults.

M: I would agree with this. I would also suggest the introduction of stricter identity checks at the point of sale and a wider application of the age-rating system. Then, online games could include a red button on the screen which children or parents could click to disable the game. That would go a long way to limiting …

C: Hmm, really? Who is going to do this limiting? I don't think you understand, Dr Mancini. Why would those companies making these games limit their own market? Total revenues from the video gaming sector amounted to more than seven billion Euros, that's 6.25 billion pounds last year and in the UK, video games outsold music and other video products for the first time last year. It's like well, you know, it's the goose that has laid the golden egg. By limiting who can play the games, the companies would be killing their goose! As for online games, well I mean …

P: Sorry to interrupt Dr Cherkov, let's come to online games in a moment. I believe Erica Winters has a different perspective on this discussion.

W: Yes. Yes, I have. First, can I say that as a representative of the gaming industry we do care who plays our games and the effect. I mean, it's not all about making money. However, our own research suggests that you are all missing the ball here. We would argue that children is not the issue. Our research suggests that children are now the minority in the game-playing community.

C: Ridiculous!

B: That can't be right.

W: Please look at the document that I have provided in the folder that the audience will find on their chairs. As you can see …

AUDIOSCRIPTS

Lesson 10.3 Track 2.14

A

B: It's true that many games have a violent reputation but in fact there is no firm proof that playing them has an automatic negative impact on children's behaviour, for example by causing aggression.

M: That's correct.

B: In fact, the report suggested that …

B

M: Er, well, um …now I believe that video games are in most cases not dangerous. Over the years, we have heard er … evidence from experts on computer games and psychologists from all over …

C

M: … consider using games for educational purposes and inform children and parents about the benefits and disadvantages that these games can have.

C: No. Informing children and parents about the benefits and disadvantages does not address the issue.

D

C: I mean, it's simply ridiculous! You know, what we need is tougher regulation on these computer games, some of which have influenced violent crime among children. You know, let's not forget that. Like the mother of Stefan Pakeerah, a 14-year-old boy from Leicester …

E

P: What do you suggest?

B: Well perhaps something like preventing the sale to children of games intended for adults.

M: I would agree with this.

F

M: I would also suggest the introduction of stricter identity checks at the point of sale and a wider application of the age-rating system. Then, online games could include a red button on the screen which children or parents could click to disable the game.

G

C: It's like well, you know, it's the goose that has laid the golden egg. By limiting who can play the games, the companies would be killing their goose!

H

W: Our research suggests that children are now the minority in the game-playing community.

C: Ridiculous!

B: That can't be right.

Lesson 11.2 Track 2.15

Sally, Raj, Danny

S: We're back with our business commentators, Raj Patel and Danny Coyne. We're looking at the recent article about countries that escaped the financial crisis. What do you think?

R: Well, Sally, I think we'd like to start with UAE as this is one we both agree on. We think the writer got this unbelievably wrong.

D: Yes, it seems to be that everyone believes that Arab economies can combat everything … you know they've got oil so they're safe, kind of thing. Well, you can argue that UAE has done pretty well, provided that you don't look too closely at what's been happening in Dubai.

R: Yes, particularly in Dubai, it has had a terrible last couple of years in the construction industry and in real estate. Where this country was once booming, now hardly anything is getting built.

S: OK, guys, but unless I'm hearing you wrong, you're talking just about Dubai?

R: Well, that's true. The UAE's strength and weakness is that it is a collection of small states and Dubai is very different from the rest.

D: What we're trying to say is that even if the UAE is doing much better than other countries round the club, it is still having problems in its economy. It's not all good news.

R: And it is less affected by what is happening outside the country than others.

D: Yes, it's still had a pretty tough time recently.

R: Yes. Let's talk about Brazil. I don't think Brazil is doing too well either. In one week last year the currency was devalued by 20 percent. That doesn't strike me as successful.

D: Well, we agree to disagree here. Yes, there was that sudden drop but it was a result of political issues, not economic ones. But for that one expected event last year, Brazil would have been seen as totally untouched by financial difficulties these past two years. This is mainly because its market is so diversified. Where I do disagree with the writer is that Brazil is not alone and is not the best example in the region. Supposing you went up to a map, closed your eyes and put a pin in any country in Latin America. You'd be pretty sure to pick a country that has done well in recent years. The whole of Latin America is a success story.

R: You know the thing that interests me is that the one country the author doesn't mention is India, and India has probably been one of the most successful markets in recent years.

S: What about Romania?

R: I have absolutely no idea whether or not Romania is doing well.

D: Me neither.

R: I would have assumed that they were having a tough time if I hadn't read this article. But I do know that Romania doesn't have a big arms industry. There are other Eastern European countries that can rely on this just as much, so if Romania is doing well I don't think it's got much to do with selling weapons. I certainly wouldn't invest in Romania just yet in case this turns out to be totally wrong. I'd want more evidence.

D: Where we both agree is with China. It really is no contest. China seems to be pretty much untouched and is coming out as the big winner. Considering its vast resources and financial potential it's really a case of crouching tiger and for the sake of the west, we hope, sleeping dragon.

S: Well, who knows. Personally, I don't care where it's made as long as it's cheap and comfortable to wear!

Lesson 11.3 Track 2.17

Right, we've talked about the ground rules of hostage negotiation. Let's now consider a subset of these negotiations, the bargaining process. More so in hostage negotiation you need this to be a win-win situation, at least the hostage-taker has to believe that they have won as much as they are going to get from the negotiation. After all we're not talking about money here, we're talking about lives and once a life is lost there's no going back. So, the bargaining process has to roll smoothly from the moment the first bid hits the table.

The bargaining rules are to make your first offer at 65 per cent of your target price and then calculating three raises, each half the amount of the previous one (20 per cent, 10 per cent, 5 per cent). These rules come from the real Godfather of international kidnapping negotiation, Mike Ackerman.

Since then, we've handed it over to others for a look and taken it a few steps further, but the basic model works for all types of negotiation across the board. Almost every negotiation I've ever seen has about three rounds to it. The form and time frame of each round varies and it takes good assessment to see where they are. That's one of the reasons that the real definition of negotiation is very close to the definition of navigation, because negotiation is moving to a goal and compromise is a poor solution. You still need to get to the goal.

Regardless of how you get there, you've got about three rounds to do it. The other side is very likely to walk away because they're simply sick of the process if you don't complete it.

If you get drawn into bargaining, don't expect to make big leaps in your position and not make the other side think that there is more room to give ground. Big jumps only make the other side hungry. It's only human nature and you ignore human nature at your peril. When you give up a lot, the other side want more.

And when they get to a goal too easily, they feel cheated and will have buyer's remorse, even if they settle. Leaving them with a bad taste in their mouth only makes them harder to deal with the next time, or worse, there's an implementation failure in the deal you've agreed to. In kidnapping negotiations, we call that a double dip. You can't sue a kidnapper so in that world we have to start again as he knows he's the only winner. And winning is addictive.

In any world, implementation failure is not a place you want to be. It takes less time to do something right than it does to do it again. If you want to speed a negotiation up, slow down.

Lesson 11.5 Track 2.18

Stephanie, Evelyn

S: Thank you Nesta for that. Now, Evelyn, I understand you have a proposal too.

E: Yes, I have Stephanie. Good afternoon everyone, my name's Evelyn Welsh and I'm sales representative for the Suffolk and Norfolk regions. The topic of my presentation is the Carry Chair. A new idea for a product. First of all, I'll tell you where the idea comes from and then I'll describe the product and then suggest why it's a really good idea. If you have any questions, please feel free to ask them at the end.

Lesson 11.5 Track 2.19

Stephanie, Evelyn, Peter, David

E: So, first of all, let me tell you where the idea came from. Do you ever go on holiday and find that by the time you get to the beach there are no deckchairs or chaises longues left? That's sunbed to you, Peter. I know I do. And the ones that are left are dirty, uncomfortable and often don't have shade. For instance, they have those small umbrellas that don't give shade to your feet or the bamboo ones with all the holes that make you look all stripy. So I thought, wouldn't it be so much better if you had one that you could take with you anywhere and that's where I got the idea from. So I've told you about the idea, let's now have a look at it. It is so easy to take with you. To illustrate my point, look at the short film I now have playing behind me. You can see that it folds up into its own suitcase and this is fully automatic.

P: But it's enormous! How heavy is that?!

E: Thank you, Peter! I'll come back to that point later, if I may. So, moving on now to the advantages. As well as automatically folding up into a travel-friendly suitcase, it comes in a variety of colours and has a side table and, as you can see this large umbrella which will protect you at all times.

D: Can we get a sponsor on the umbrella ...?

E: As I was about to say ... what does this mean for our marketing division? Well, we can get sponsors for the umbrella and sell advertising space. Right, well I'd like to recap by saying that the Carry Chair is perfect for anyone wanting sun, sea and sand but not getting burnt to a crisp. It is easy to take with you and isn't that expensive to make ...

D: Er, just how much ...?

E: Thank you everyone for coming to my presentation!

Lesson 12.2 Track 2.20

A: Contemporary society is a guilty pleasure, but a pleasure nonetheless. And this is how most people see it. They have been given a quality of life unrivalled in the history of civilization. The idea of it coming to the end is too horrific to contemplate. So they don't bother with it. This is exactly why any such doomsday scenario like Peak Oil has little chance of affecting government policies or the human psyche.

B: Well, I'll tell you I've had it up to here with the anti-plastic brigade! It's the exact opposite that is needed, that is, we need access to more domestic resources to meet the demands of our society. And why are people so worried about the price of petrol? Let's compare the price of petrol that I sell, at two pounds a gallon with several other popular products: Häagen-Dazs vanilla ice cream costs 18 pounds a gallon, A Starbucks House Blend coffee 12 pounds a gallon, Evian water five pounds per gallon. Petrol is cheaper than water. I don't think we're going to see Peak Oil for a long time to come. And when we do, it won't be because we're running out of oil. It will be because we prefer other technologies. Right now I assure, you, oil production is not running out. The sooner the tree-huggers stop ranting, the better.

C: In all the years I have covered the story of oil I have never seen a situation like the one we now find ourselves in. As oil becomes more and more expensive it becomes further and further out of reach of the middle class. Therefore, it's not easy to be hopeful that we're going to face these things politically. The situation is bonkers. The global peak of new oil discoveries took place back in 1964; the world has been burning more oil than it finds every year since 1981; and so far, less oil has been discovered this decade than in any since the 1930s.

D: There's always people spouting this stuff. As I understand it, we've got lots of oil and we're barely halfway to running out of it. That gives a huge amount of time to deal with it. No, I'm not worried. I don't understand the whole thing but human beings are natural survivors. Look at the atom bomb. It's never been used because the human knows when to stop. It'll be the same with oil. I have great faith in our ability to survive.

E: Humans use more oil each day than we breathe oxygen. We are petroleum people. And so the future – what is the future of the oil tribe? That's exactly it. We will soon revert to a tribal culture. This stuff is going to get more expensive, and as it does our lives will slowly fall apart. My grandchildren will probably have less of a good life than my great-great-grandparents!

F: Well, the dirt you see here today, someone will be putting in their car in six days. Sounds great doesn't it? It isn't. Whenever doubts are raised about this site, the same argument is wheeled out. And to be fair it's correct. The oil sands do make oil. They are economic. You can expand them. However, the argument glosses over the truth. There's a lot of oil there, but you're going to produce it over centuries, not decades. It's going to come out slowly and steadily. So if Peak Oil comes about, oil sands are not going to rescue us.

Lesson 12.3 Track 2.22

1 There is no one thing but a combination of things that need to be considered in tandem. Firstly, call a professional extermination firm. Don't try to kill the bugs yourself: last year an American woman blew up her home trying to kill bedbugs. Don't throw away your furniture. The chances are that you will spread the bugs through your home. Don't flee the infested room. The bedbugs want food and warmth: if you go, they'll follow. Talk to your neighbours. It's possible your bugs have come from them, or that you have given them yours. Finally, don't panic. Bedbugs don't carry diseases, and their presence does not make you unclean.

2 Well, yes they were. However, the bugs have made a recent comeback. Some research indicates that up to 25 per cent of residents in some cities have reported problems with them; usually in lower-class, urban areas. For these residents, bed-bugs are not only a nuisance, but a problem bordering on epidemic levels.

3 The world saw a marked decrease in the numbers of bedbugs when DDT was introduced in the 1950s. The use of DDT as a pesticide was banned in the 1970s and hardy bed bugs seemingly welcomed the news. In the past few years, levels of bedbug infestations have been rising alarmingly. Also, with increased world travel, bedbugs are again making their presence felt as they are removed from one country and introduced to another through international transport on clothing, luggage and the human body. Bedbugs can be found on airlines and in cargo holds. Bedbugs can also be transferred from an overnight stay in hotels, motels and inns.

4 There are probably three things. Look for unexplained rashes, although one in ten people doesn't respond to bites. If you react badly, see a doctor. Check your sheets for bloodstains: you may have rolled over and crushed a bug after it has fed on you. If you have a severe infestation, you might notice a sweet smell around your bed frame.

5 Well, it's very long indeed. We can find evidence of bugs infesting beds in the earliest writings dating back thousands of years. They are very resilient insects. Certainly they became a major phenomenon with the advent of major shipping lanes traversing the world. It seems there was no history of bedbugs in the United States until larger quantities of colonists arrived there.

Lesson 12.4 Track 2.23

It is quite clear to me, based on my research, that tropical insects rather than polar bears could be among the first species to become extinct as a result of global warming.

Insects in the tropics are already living at their, at the limit of their temperature range and any further increases could quickly kill them off. This would be a major disaster for tropical habitats, which rely on insects for everything from pollination to waste disposal. We have found that a rise in average temperatures in the tropics of just one or two degrees Celsius could be enough to exert a significant and harmful effect on the survival of a wide variety of important insects. Fitness levels most likely decline quickly and there may not be much we can do about it.

Many tropical species can only tolerate a narrow range of temperatures because the climate they experience is pretty constant throughout the year. Now our calculations show that they will be harmed by rising temperatures more than would species in cold climates. Unfortunately, the tropics also hold the large majority of species on the planet.

We used daily and monthly global temperatures from the 50 year period between 1950 and 2000 and compared them against data showing the fitness of different species.

'Fitness' was determined by indicators such as population growth rates and physical performance for different creatures.

We found that even moving into the shade did not help the insects. The direct effects of climate change on the organisms we studied appear to depend a lot more on the organisms' flexibility than on the amount of warming in the area where they lived.

As well as the danger for insects, the research confirms that there will be other consequences of global warming that could also have a serious impact on tropical regions, particularly on food crops. Our research focused only on the impact of changes in temperature, but warming also will alter rainfall patterns. These changes could be more important for many tropical organisms, such as plants, but they are harder to predict.

ANSWER KEY

Unit 1 Lesson 1

1
1 dumbing down
2 assessments
3 interpersonal skills
4 plagiarism
5 curriculum
6 streaming
7 elitism

2
1 elitism
2 interpersonal skills
3 dumbing down
5 plagiarism
5 curriculum
6 assessments
7 streaming

4
1 loose cannon
2 all-rounder
3 high-flier
5 dark horse

Unit 1 Lesson 2

1
1 C
2 F
3 E
4 A
5 D
6 B

2
1 I'm doing, is always buying, standing still, doing something wrong, responding, painting the pole, we're coming, knowing, will be, moving

3
1 were coming
2 I'm doing something right / I'm doing something wrong / is always buying
3 had been blocking
4 will be moving

4
1 He finally got through to the operator after he had been trying for over two hours.
2 The research on the behaviour of students in exams has been going on for several years.
3 I was thinking about the offer all night.
4 The examinations are being planned for Thursday at 10 a.m.
5 The whole of this month, we are having negotiations between ourselves and the Dickson Group.

5
1 E
2 –
3 B/E
4 A
5 –
6 B
7 C
8 D
9 A/F

6
1 accomplished ✓
2 affectionate ✓
3 allergic ✓
4 ambitious ✓
5 educational ✓
7 famous ✓
10 passionate ✓
11 persuasive ✓
13 powerful ✓
15 skilful ✓
16 successful ✓
17 superstitious ✓
18 toxic ✓

7
1 photography
2 accomplish
3 affectionately
4 fiction
5 allergic
6 superstition
7 ambition
8 Fame
9 grammar
10 toxins

Unit 1 Lesson 3

1a Track 1.4
Well, I've just finished my BA in English Language and Literature. Certainly for the next year, I'm not thinking of postgraduate work. Having said that, I'm not ruling it out. It's just I'm not sure whether I want to do an MA or an MBA. I have no intention of doing a PhD. It'll just take up too much of my life. I have already taken IELTs, when I applied to study at Reading and I don't think a BEC will help me right now.

1b
1 a recent graduate / graduate
2 He's just finished a degree.
3 a PhD.

2
1 c
2 a
3 b
4 c
5 a

3
1 Having said
2 hadn't thought about
3 to have finished
4 will have been working
5 had been thinking
6 have been fluctuating
7 have been fighting

4
1 past perfect
2 future perfect
3 present perfect

5
1 Having read
2 Having discussed
3 to have solved
4 having met
5 to have fixed
6 to have done

6
C. It is not about students

7
1 A
2 D
3 C
4 B

8
True statements: 1, 3

Unit 1 Lesson 4

1
1 a summer job
2 students, young people

2
1 Let me start by saying that age is a pre-requisite.
2 I think it's absolutely essential that they are fit.
3 It would be helpful if they had done some previous work with kids.
4 It would probably give them an edge.
5 They have to have interpersonal skills.
6 They must have discipline.
7 It'd be a good thing if the've been involved in social groups.
8 It's essential that they can sing round campfires.
9 Some climbing skills would be an advantage.

4

1 worked in summer camps before
2 quality / confidence
3 I like / a lot of discipline
4 asset / that he is very fit
5 disadvantages / drawbacks / she is
  not very fit
6 am concerned / worried that / any
  foreign languages
7 worried about / age
8 concerns me / worries me / of
  friendliness / personality

Unit 1 Lesson 5

1

Letter A
1 E
2 G
3 B
4 F

Letter B
5 H
6 C
7 D
8 A

2

1 Letter B
2 Letter A
3 in the Guardian newspaper
4 at any time
5 He attended two extra summer
  courses in the industry.

3

(example)

Dear _____

I am writing to enquire if you have
any vacancies. I enclose my CV for
your information. I have just finished
university with a first class degree
and am keen to start work as soon as
possible. I am loyal, committed and
highly motivated. I also have lots of
ideas, some examples of which can be
found on my website.

I would like to work for a company with
a great reputation and high profile like
[insert company name].

I have excellent references and would
be delighted to discuss any possible
vacancy with you at your convenience.
In case you do not have any suitable
openings at the moment, I would be
grateful if you would keep my CV on
file for any future possibilities.

Yours sincerely,

Unit 2 Lesson 1

1

1 carbon
2 excursions
3 ancient
4 delights
5 last-minute
6 temperatures
7 airline
8 hotel

2

1 boutique hotel
2 last-minute deals
3 baking temperatures
4 organised excursions
5 gastronomic delights
6 ancient monument
7 carbon footprint
8 budget airlines

3

1 get away from it all
2 steer clear of the tourist traps
3 get back to nature
4 lounge around by the pool

Unit 2 Lesson 2

1

1 C
2 H
3 F
4 E

2

1 rejuvenation
2 morbid
3 proximity
4 decimated
5 pampering
6 flock
7 awe
8 pretentious
9 niche
10 recuperation

3

1 paragraph 6
2 paragraph 13
3 paragraph 4
4 paragraph 9
5 paragraph 5
6 paragraph 11
7 paragraph 2

4

1 a
2 the
3 a
4 The
5 the
6 a
7 an
8 the
9 the
10 a

Unit 2 Lesson 3

1a Track 1.7

Later tonight, on this week's edition
of Saving the World, Jack Harper will
be looking into the Volunteer Tourism
Industry where, as opposed to lounging
by the pool and soaking up the sun,
young people usually go off the beaten
track, particularly to developing
countries and try to do something for
those who may be less well off than
themselves. But is that really the case?
Jack Harper will be joined by some of
the big names in the Volunteer Tourism
industry to investigate this further.

1b

1 A presenter
2 Jack Harper
3 the volunteer tourism industry

2

Students' own answers

3

1 T
2 –
3 R
4 T
5 J
6 T
7 R
8 R

4

1 This could spell bad news.
2 Unskilled Brits may do more harm
  than good.
3 … can take advantage of this.
4 Even the retired might soon start
  signing up
5 Young people could be better off
  travelling …
6 They'll put them in contact with
  recently returned volunteers.
7 Volunteers had to work as office
  staff.

5

1 I don't think we can sell the
  computer this month.
2 You shouldn't make a last-minute
  deal.
3 They would like to change the date
  of the excursion to 13 June.
4 She may / might be lounging by the
  pool.
5 You ought not to / mustn't sit on the
  beach in baking temperatures.
6 If you are not careful, you may /
  might be / get ripped off.
7 Of course we will arrange an
  excursion off the beaten track.

Unit 2 Lesson 4

1

1 Gavin Glover, the Project Manager of the Falmer Community Stadium Project.
2 People representing the football club, the council, the conservation society and the local villagers.
3 To discuss whether a new stadium should be built.
4 To find a solution that is acceptable to the different interested parties.

2

1 absolute / for
2 possible
3 position / clear
4 been / clear
5 exactly / mean
6 is / negotiable
7 understand / coming
8 vital / if
9 If / understand
10 seems to me / won't

4

1 D
2 A
3 C
4 B
5 C
6 B

Unit 2 Lesson 5

1

1 Compare
2 Account for
3 Outline
4 Define
5 Assess
6 Analyse
7 Critically evaluate

2

a Situation
b Problem
c Solution
d Implication
e Solution
f Problem
g Solution
h Implication

3

1 Moreover
2 As a result
3 For instance
4 because of this
5 On the other hand

Unit 3 Lesson 1

1

1 love of
2 proud of
3 ability to
4 obsession with
5 great at
6 fascination with
7 reluctance to
8 passion for

2

1 aloof
2 pragmatic
3 devious
4 confident
5 self-effacing
6 meticulous
7 cultured
8 zealous
9 hospitable
10 optimistic

Unit 3 Lesson 2

1a Track 1.11

Interpol, whose full name is the International Criminal Police Organization, is an organisation facilitating international police cooperation in crimes that overlap several member countries. Its work focuses primarily on public safety, terrorism, organised crime and war crimes but not political, military, religious or racial crimes.

1b

1 The work of Interpol.
2 It helps police forces co-operate on crimes committed in different countries.
3 It can't help solve political, military, religious or racial crimes.

2

1 One aim of the conference is to improve **co-operation** between police forces all over **Africa**.
2 Egyptian police have worked with Interpol to ensure convictions for **selling counterfeit medicines**.
3 The Nairobi office of Interpol will **play a key role** in chasing and arresting pirates.

3

1 President Khoo Boon Hui
2 General Ronald K. Noble
3 Egyptian First Assistant Minister of the Interior Adly Fayed
4 General Ronald K. Noble
5 INTERPOL President Khoo Boon Hui

4

1 cause / reason
2 non-defining relative clause
3 purpose
4 adverbial
5 condition

5

1 Provided
2 in order to
3 that
4 As soon as
5 who
6 so
7 Since

6

1 they haven't watched the news this week.
2 requested his arrest.
3 (that) people don't know about the possible damage.
4 there is not enough evidence to convict him.
5 he was accused of stealing
6 might be innocent
7 make judgements about what is right or wrong.

Unit 3 Lesson 3

1

1 place
2 in another country
3 is only in the capital

2

1 amabssadorial work is done / live there
2 considered the other important enough
3 High Commissions
4 Sanctuary

3

1 seen
4 lived
6 had
7 seen

4

1 ought to have
2 must have
3 needn't have
4 could have

5

1 can't have heard
2 should have seen
3 might have discovered
4 needn't have postponed
5 must have got
6 could have gone
7 oughtn't to have / shouldn't have taken
8 shouldn't have caused
9 can't have been made
10 ought to have known / should have known

6

1 A
2 D
3 E
4 C
5 B

7

3 Career diplomats spend over two thirds of their time abroad.
5 Oman has an Msc in Middle Eastern politics.
6 You may work in different sectors or countries.

Unit 3 Lesson 4

1

1 The islands are being used for terrorism.
2 A Minister and an Ambassador.
3 The minister is planning a military action.
4 It will be seen as an attack on the Ambassador's country.
5 There will be a war.

2

1 objective
2 goals
3 priority
4 aim to
5 key

3

A 5
B 4
C 2
D 3
E 1

4a

1 advisable
2 ought
3 essential
4 ought
5 recommend
6 advise

4b

1 ... consider the possible results of such an action.
2 ... understand that these terrorists can be just as much a threat to your country as they are to ours.
3 ... remove these terrorists from our border as quickly as possible.
4 ... consider other options.
5 ... do not forget the danger to our people ...
6 ... reconsider this action and find a solution that does not involve ...

Unit 3 Lesson 5

1

1 –
2 B
3 A
4 B
5 B
6 A
7 A
8 B
9 –
10 A

2

Students' own answers

3

Speaker A - The Minister

4

1 alliteration <u>men not mice</u>
5 rhetorical questions <u>What would you have this government do?</u>
6 tripling <u>peace, protection and prosperity</u>

Unit 4 Lesson 1

1

chest pains
blood pressure
heart surgery
flu virus
premature ageing
high salt intake

2

1 immune system
2 infant mortality
3 life expectancy
4 maternity ward
5 tanning salon

3

1 life expectancy
2 high salt intake
3 flu virus
4 maternity ward
5 infant mortality
6 immune system
7 blood pressure
8 chest pains
9 heart surgery
10 tanning salon
11 premature ageing

Unit 4 Lesson 2

1

1 in the letters column of a newspaper
2 to respond to an article
3 The National Health Service

2

1 medical services / everyone
2 fully covered / partially covered
3 a wider range of services
4 has a choice / treatment
5 many people believe / alternative medicine.
6 a quality service

3

Notion	Linker
Addition	Furthermore
	and
	as
Contrast	but
	However
Causal	As a result
Temporal	When
	After that

5

1 As
2 In addtion / Moreover
3 However
4 Although
5 After
6 until
7 nevertheless

6

1 C
2 C
3 R
4 R
5 C
6 R
7 R
8 C

7

1 radio debate
2 Students' own answers
3 State sector: A, B, C, D
  Private Sector: E, F, G, H, I
4 Students' own answers

8

1 GP
2 clinic
3 check-up
4 lack of funding
5 pharmacist
6 preventative

Unit 4 Lesson 3

1a Track 1.16

Doctors Without Borders, is a secular humanitarian-aid non-governmental organisation best known for its projects in war-torn regions and developing countries facing endemic disease.

The organisation was created in 1971 by a small group of French doctors, who believed that all people have the right to medical care regardless of race, religion, belief or political affiliation, and that the needs of these people should not be refused due to national borders.

1b

1 the medical charity Doctors Without Borders
2 to provide medical services to people in refugee camps
3 It works all over the world

2

1 E
2 D
3 F
4 H
5 I
6 C
7 H
8 B
9 G

3a

Positive meaning: exhilarating, invigorating, inspiring, elated, relieved, rejuvenated

Negative meaning: disillusioned, antagonised, disorientated

3b

1 antagonised
2 disillusioned
3 disorientated
4 elated
5 relieved

4

1 There has been an earthquake.
2 To go into the earthquake zone and provide medical services.
3 To assess the situation and decide what teams are needed.
4 The supplies team.
5 To increase their sales in the region.
6 To complete the estimate of how many medical staff are needed.

5 and 6

1 be due to
2 be about to
3 likely to be
4 be bound to
5 to be + infinitive is not used

7

1 The old medical cards are to be discontinued from January 1st.
2 His scan is about to be performed.
3 Appointments are not to be made after 6pm.
4 It's likely she will be able to go home next week.
5 The government is bound to increase the health budget today.
6 The Health Minister is due to make a statement at 15.30.
7 She told him to stop just as he was about to take the wrong pill.

Unit 4 Lesson 4

1

1 b
2 c
3 a
4 c

2

1 While I accept that / it would also be
2 the fact that / means that / is fully justified
3 If we do / people will inevitably
4 the kind of thing
5 you can see / can't you
6 may well ask
7 I mean that
8 One reason I favour

Unit 4 Lesson 5

1

1 How people reduce stress levels.
2 From a medical survey, or official statistics.
3 Women have done slightly more.

2

Sample answer

The charts show the results of research in Hong Kong to find out if people do anything to reduce stress and, if so, what they do to reduce it.

Overall, the chart shows that only about 50 percent of people actually do anything to reduce stress. Of the people who do something to reduce stress, only around 5 percent make a significant effort. There seems to be little difference between the behaviour of men and the behaviour of women in this regard.

Unit 5 Lesson 1

1

materialism, mall, phenomenom, breed

2

1 confidence
2 advice
3 supply
4 boom
5 groups
6 spending
7 choice
8 trends
9 demand
10 products / goods
11 products / goods

3

A 7
B 11
C 10
D 6
E 9
F 3
G 1
H 4
I 8
J 2
K 5

Unit 5 Lesson 2

1

1 Milan is the new fashion capital.
2 The survey makes its decision based on counting the frequency of words and phrases across the media world.
3 The previous fashion capital was number 1 for five years.
6 The reason for the city's success is that is has Prada.

2

Best title is 3, Prada: From suitcases to catwalk, From Milan to the world

3

1 C
2 H
3 F
4 I
5 A
6 B
7 D
8 E
9 G

4

1 fashion-conscious
2 eye-catching
  time-consuming
3 hand-made
4 big-name

5

1 D
2 B
3 A
4 C

6

1 were meant to
2 was / due to
3 was going to
4 would
5 was going to
6 was bound to
7 were going to
8 would

Unit 5 Lesson 3

1 Track 1.20

Fashion is seen in our consciousness as a glamour thing. It's all about beauty, happy people having fun and getting to wear the best clothes. People who actually work in the industry see it very differently. They all agree that working in fashion is an obsession, but that is pretty much the only reason to work there. The pay, the hours, the way you are treated would not be enough to sustain the motivation required in this cut-throat industry.

2

consciousness, obsession, motivation

3

NOUN	VERB	ADJECTIVE	ADVERB
obsession	obsess	obsessive	obsessively
action	act	active	actively
consciousness	—	conscious	consciously
convenience	—	convenient	conveniently
popularity	—	popular	popularly
sustainability	sustain	sustainable	sustainably
violation	violate	violated	—
happiness	—	happy	happily
confidence	—	confident	confidently
tendency	tend	—	—
possibility	—	possible	possibly

4

1 violation
2 convenience
3 consciousness
4 popularity

5

1 Nelly
2 Alicia
3 Alicia
4 Alicia
5 Nelly
6 Alicia

6

1 Helen
2 All
3 Raymond
4 Raymond
5 Raymond and Helen
6 Luca
7 Luca

7

Nelly Sykes Fashion stylist

Alicia Jackson Couture designer

Raymond Heinze Fashion Zine editor

Helen Mumtaz Fashion designer

Luca Canegallo Menswear designer

8

1 Never is anything typical in the world of fashion.
2 With haute couture, compromise is never an option.
3 It's getting the timing right – that is the big problem.
4 What this means is steaming garments.

9

1 What fashion designers do is make art out of nothing.
2 No sooner had I got through the door when Vivienne rang and …
3 What I adore are her latest designs.
4 It's actually rather dull – modelling.
5 What I really need is to get 100 metres of pink lace by yesterday.
6 At no time did he know that the designs had already been copied.
7 What they did was take a taxi from the station.

Unit 5 Lesson 4

1

A would be
B we were to / we'd
C need to / otherwise we'd
D was wondering if
E suppose we did get / wouldn't
F sure how feasible
G we were to / still keep
H that'd mean
I mean that we'd have to
J Surely it'd be better

2

Order of sentences: F, D, A, I, B, J, H, E (C and G not used)

Unit 5 Lesson 5

1

1 c
2 d

3

1 haute couture
2 Paris couture season
3 buttons and lace
4 the process
5 famous actress
6 Christian Dior
7 haute couture

Unit 6 Lesson 1

1

1 state-of-the art
2 old-hat
3 innovative
4 revolutionary
5 new-fangled
6 outdated
7 redundant
8 cutting edge
9 retro
10 obsolete
11 behind-the-times
12 outmoded
13 ground-breaking
14 pioneering

2

Positive meaning
state-of-the art, innovative,
revolutionary, cutting edge,
ground-breaking, pioneering
Negative meaning
old-hat, new-fangled, outdated,
redundant, retro, obsolete,
behind-the-times, outmoded

3

1 account
2 impact
3 expansion
4 results
5 contribute
6 is leading
7 a rise
8 stems

Unit 6 Lesson 2

1

1 E
2 A
3 D
4 B
5 C

2

Electronic skin
are networked
The next plalstic
which is made from orange rinds
can be turned
can be made
can be produced

4

1 Three million pounds has been
awarded for copyright infringement
by the court.
2 Tests are still continuing on their
prototype.
3 He was really disappointed when he
was told the decision of the panel.
4 The implication of this development
will need to be discussed at the next
meeting.
5 The idea of burying CO_2 in the sea is
being considered by the government.
6 The project is being funded by the
Association for the Revival of Serious
Ecological Development.

5a

1 a lecturer
2 students
3 to research three of the ideas

5b

1 Idea 2
2 Idea 1
3 Idea 3
4 Idea 1
5 Idea 3
6 Idea 2

Unit 6 Lesson 3

1

1 on like a house on fire
2 on / nerves
3 him down
4 off to / start
5 the hang of

2

1 A conference
2 A scientist
3 She is worried about the prospect
of the effects on human life of robot
technology.
4 The new book by Ray Kurzweil.

3

True statements: 1, 4, 5, 6, 7

4

A I had the organisers rearrange this
plenary
B I have had my fears of the ethical
dimensions challenged.
C The subject they started discussing
made me take note immediately.
D Ray let me have an early copy of his
book *The Age of Spiritual Machines*,
which outlined a utopia he predicted
E With Ray's kind permission, I have
been allowed to reproduce the
handouts in front of you.

5

1 B
2 D
3 E
4 C
5 A

6

1 made us wait
2 published a book
3 not allowed
4 was fined
5 let you use
6 were made to
7 had the designs destroyed

7

Correct points 2, 3, 4, 5, 6, 8

8

1 unimportant – superfluous
2 predictions – conjectures
3 destroy – exterminate
4 control – oversight
5 kind – humane
6 kept – retained
7 good or suitable – wholesome
8 assume – postulate
9 load or responsibility – burden
10 majority of the population – masses

Unit 6 Lesson 4

1

Photo C

2

A I think the facts speak for themselves,
don't they?
B The total number is over a million,
yes, one million.
C It's incredible what this little thing
does.
D I'm sure you would agree that
Teleblok is an extraordinarily
versatile piece of equipment.
E Let me start by giving you an
amazing statistic.
F And I'd just like to give you one other
striking example.

3a

1 E
2 C
3 D
4 F
5 B
6 A

3b

1 Teleblok.
2 A piece of equipment which blocks annoying calls.
3 Because there are so many annoying calls.
4 It is expensive.
5 It could be sold as part of a telephone / people already pay £40 a year for a similar service.
6 The name.
7 Students' own answer.

Unit 6 Lesson 5

1

1 that you attach to your phone
2 asking for permission from you
3 will block up to 5000 calls
4 costs £97
5 more expensive

2

verification verify verified / verifable verifiably – approved

consumption consume consumed – take up

liberation liberate liberated – free

inclination incline inclined – curiosity

3

Sample Answer

Tired of calls upsetting your daily life?

Want strangers to leave you alone?

Don't want to answer every call?

Wouldn't your life be easier if all of this was done for you?

Teleblok is a little machine that connects to your phone. It answers your calls, identifies the caller, asks you if you want to speak to the caller and, if you don't accept, it will block the caller. It can also block all future calls from the same caller. Teleblok will remove from your life all those telephone calls that take up your time and is less expensive in the long-term than the service other telephone companies provide.

Teleblok will

- block up to **5000** calls.

- save you money

- save you time.

Here is what one person said:

'Before Teleblok, I was dealing with **20** annoying calls a days. Now I don't have any at all.' (Anna Dahl)

Teleblok price: £97 only. 3-year guarantee.

phone 01908675453 or visit www. trublok.com to try Teleblok for free

Unit 7 Lesson 1

1

a time on someone's hands
b got someone's hands full
c hand in hand
d turn someone's hand to anything
e a safe pair of hands
f on hand

2

1 d
2 a
3 c
4 b
5 g
6 f

3

1 arrogant
2 selfish
3 insular
4 romantic
5 emotional
6 unrealistic
7 sensitive

4

True statements: 2, 4, 5

Unit 7 Lesson 2

1a Track 2.2

With the exception of the great work being done in the Arab world and, to a certain extent, in China, human development in terms of scientific understanding and the development of technology had been stagnant since the end of the Roman Empire. It is with the Renaissance in the 15th century that a new period of growth really started. Yet, where do we date the exact beginning of the Scientific Revolution? Undoubtedly that begins with Nicolaus Copernicus and the publication of his theory of space that literally changed the way we see the earth and the universe and inspired the later work of Galileo.

1b

1 The end of the Roman Empire
2 Development in the Middle and Far East
3 The beginning of the Renaissance movement
4 Copernicus's theory
5 Galileo

2

astronomer, doctor, scholar, economist, military leader, diplomat

3

1 F
2 T
3 F
4 T
5 T
6 NT
7 NT
8 F

4

1 reform
2 defining
3 circulation
4 adopted
5 stroke
6 formulate
7 besieged
8 legend
9 subsequent
10 vocation

5

+ **singular noun:** either, every, no, none

uncountable/plural: many, some, any, (a) few, most, several, all, (a) little both, a lot of, much

6

1 a lot of / most
2 No
3 any
4 None
5 Either
6 Few

Unit 7 Lesson 3

1

A farming
B consciousness
C $E=mc^2$
D vaccination
E human rights
F world wide web
G zero
H gravity

2

1 world wide web
2 gravity
3 zero
4 conciousness
5 human rights
6 zero
7 $E=MC^2$
8 vaccination

3

1 apocryphal
2 handy
3 traced back to
4 flawlessly
5 myriad
6 batted around
7 antibodies

4

1 government, trading and individual specialisation
2 in books, comics and films in popular culture
3 wash their hands
4 numbers
5 live longer

5

1 didn't / would
2 open / find
3 hadn't been discovered / wouldn't have nuclear power
4 don't have / don't have
5 hadn't come along / wouldn't have had

6

a If you open any book, comic or watch any film in popular culture, you find the unconscious.
b If we don't have numbers, we don't have mathematics.
c If farming didn't exist, then neither would development.
d If vaccines hadn't been invented, I probably would have died years ago.
e If it hadn't been discovered, we wouldn't have nuclear power

7

1 c
2 e
3 d
4 b
5 a

8

1 If the Senator had listened to his wife and stayed at home, he wouldn't have been assassinated.
2 If he provides evidence, we will publish his theory.
3 If you cannot attend, you should inform us as soon as possible.
4 If I did not know the story was apocryphal, then I would believe you.
5 If you can get funding for your project, then we would be able to reconsider our decision.

Unit 7 Lesson 4

1

A It might not be such a big problem.
B I can see some real problems.
C I just don't think it's feasible.
D I think it's a really good suggestion.
E It may not cost as much as you think.
F Will it really work?
G In my opinion, it's a good project.
H I'm not too keen on this one.
I It sounds like a great idea!
J It could be a very expensive option.
K Some of the projects must be long term.

2

1 B / C / D / G / H / I
2 B / C / H / J / K
3 C / F
4 A / E
5 B / C / F / H / J / K
6 B / C / H

Unit 7 Lesson 5

1

1 the quality of education
2 that students are lazy
3 She sounds annoyed.
4 Students' own answers.

2

3 Why spend so much money …
4 We need to change …
5 College is all about growing up and gaining resposibility.
6 Lazy students are able to pressure professors.
7 Our country could get worse.

3

Students' own answers

Unit 8 Lesson 1

1

1 chequebook journalism
2 viewing figures
3 media coverage
4 ratings wars
5 libel laws
6 circulation figures

2

1 privacy
2 speculation
3 broadsheet
4 tabloid
5 soundbite
6 bias
7 spin
8 deadline
9 source
10 scoop

3

1 mass circulation
2 press coverage
3 scoop
4 source
5 media coverage
6 libel laws
7 chequebook journalism
8 privacy
9 tabloid
10 broadsheet
11 ratings wars

4

1 c
2 c
3 b
4 d
5 a

Unit 8 Lesson 2

1a Track 2.5

Last night on the radio I listened to a very sloppy interviewee. This aspiring pop star was totally uninhibited in his answers. Instead of being succinct and objective, his answers were totally subjective and many were superfluous to the subject. However, although the interview was one of the most deplorable I have ever heard, it was invaluable for me because I can use it on my training course next month.

1b

1 a journalist
2 an interview on the radio
3 the answers were not relevant

2

1 E
2 C
3 B
4 F
5 A
6 D

3

1 Find out / before
2 answer / you want to
3 say things / printed
4 just doing their job
5 give / information
6 everything you say
7 Scripting / preparing
8 off the record
9 experienced / avoid live interviews

ANSWER KEY

4

1 … journalists cannot make you answer
2 … invites you to talk / … and really want to explore
3 … you might consider scripting what you're going to say
4 think about going off the record
5 … before you even start talking

5

1 awarded / writing
2 like working
3 considered working
4 urged / tell
5 made / do
6 promise / will drive
7 heard / leaving

6

Correct statements: 2, 3, 4, 8

7a–b

Students' own answers

Unit 8 Lesson 3

1a–b

1 So is this confidential? **Y**
2 Can my boss stop us using Facebook at work? **Y**
3 Can my boss discipline me for using social networking sites during work time? **Y**
4 Can my employer monitor what I'm writing on Facebook whilst I'm at work? **D**
5 Can an employer refuse to appoint me to a job because of my Facebook profile? **N**
6 Should I accept a Facebook friend request from my boss? **D**

2

keep a close eye on, keep an open mind, keep in with

3

1 your wits about you
2 an eye on
3 keep your fingers crossed
4 an open mind
5 a low profile

5

1 The use of social networking sites at work.
2 Because they can learn from what other companies are doing.
3 Not to ban the use of social networking sites at work.
4 It comes from a professional report.
5 The sites can help companies make contacts across the market and develop new business.

6

1 c
2 a
3 b
4 a
5 c

7

1 deal with
2 brought out
3 think about
4 come up with
5 clam up
6 getting through
7 take a look into
8 accused of
9 take a good look at

8

1 got over
2 get through / clams up
3 look into
4 come up with
5 come across
6 dealt with
7 accuse / of

Unit 8 Lesson 4

1

A 5
B 4
C 8
D 1
E 2
F 7
G 6
H 3

2

1 B
2 D
3 E
4 H
5 F
6 A
7 G
8 C

Unit 8 Lesson 5

1

1 B
2 A
3 C
4 D
5 C

2

Texts 3 and 5 are unreliable as they are based on opinion and not fact.

3

1 D
2 B
3 A
4 C

Unit 9 Unit 1

1

1 c
2 e
3 g
4 h
5 a
6 i
7 d
8 f
9 b

2

A 7
B 3
C 6
D 9
E 1
F 8
G 2
H 4
I 5

3

1 system
2 behaviour
3 economic
4 the use of something
5 a law
6 youth

4

1 restrict / tighten
2 justice
3 anti-social
4 policy
5 concern
6 class
7 migrants
8 crime

ANSWER KEY

Unit 9 Lesson 2

1
1 offenders
2 courts
3 deter
4 rehabilitation
5 custodial
6 community
7 care
8 deterrent
9 delinquency
10 punishment

2a
a) 3-5
b) 2-5
c) 0-2, 6-8
d) 0-2
e) all
f) 3-5
g) 0-2
h) 3-5
i) 0-2
j) 3-5

3
1 j
2 f
3 h
4 c

4
Adverbs with gradable adjectives
extremely really hardly fairly
Adverbs with ungradable adjectives
utterly

6
1 She is too highly qualified for this post.
2 He was extremely / quite lucky to get his promotion.
3 Your response to the question is totally unacceptable.
4 It is extremely unlikely / entirely possible that he will be arrested.
5 It is absolutely necessary for you to be there.

7
1 reinforcements
2 positive reinforcement
3 something that is unpleasant
4 nagging will stop
5 to get rid of
6 negative

8
1 a) Smacking teaches children that it is OK to hurt people.
   b) It only works if the punisher is present.
2 It is not only a punishment but also teaches the child a lesson.

Unit 9 Lesson 3

1a Track 2.10
Over the last 60 years, people from other places in the international community have come to Britain to find a new life. As time passes these small communities do their best to try and integrate into British culture with mixed success. This week, we'll be analysing the experiences of one such group, the Turkish community, and seeing what challenges they have faced, how they have dealt with them and whether they have achieved a measure of integration or not.

1b
1 d)
2 b)

2
True statements: 1, 2, 5, 6, 7

3
1 Example given
2 Many migrants said they came to the UK and set up shops.
3 Migrants said they worked in the UK but hoped to go home one day.
4 They said the UK and Turkey had both changed a lot.
5 They said the Turks were a very strong community.
6 They said British culture did not always provide good examples of how to live.
7 They said young people with Turkish parents feel British.

4
1 The accusation she made about me cheating was unfair.
2 Their advice to attend an English course was not useful.
3 His denial about entering the country illegally was not believed.
4 An agreement to stop arguing about the course programme has been reached.
5 Her explanation of the experiment was very clear.
6 His observation that no one had been guarding the entrance was astonishing.

Unit 9 Lesson 4

1
1 g
2 f
3 e
4 c
5 b
6 a
7 d

2
Students' own answers

Unit 9 Lesson 5

1
1 A
2 B
3 B
4 A

2a
c) Paragraph C
b) Paragraph D
a) Paragraph F
d) Paragraph H
e) Paragraph H

2b
Correct order: G, I, A, D, F, B, H, C, E

3
1 D
2 B
3 E
4 F

Unit 10 Lesson 1

1a
1 venue
2 choir
3 bill
4 adaptation
5 company
6 trio
7 virtuoso
8 choreographer

1b
1 venue
2 bill
3 trio
4 choreographer
5 adaptation
6 company
7 virtuoso
8 choir

2a
1 star-studded
2 awe-inspiring
3 professionally-trained
4 fun-packed
5 medal-winning
6 French-born
7 out-of-the-way
8 top-heavy

ANSWER KEY

2b

1 out-of-the-way
2 awe-inspiring
3 professionally-trained
4 French-born
5 fun-packed
6 medal-winning
7 star-studded
8 top-heavy

Unit 10 Lesson 2

1a Track 2.11

The 1930s was a catastrophe for farmers in the American states of Oklahoma, Texas and Colorado. Two years of severe drought in a region that had been over farmed for years turned fields into dust which, combined with strong winds, devastated the farming communities of America. Thousands of people were driven off the land or became bankrupt. This disaster was evocatively described in the novels of John Steinbeck but the real voice of the Dust Bowl was a man who travelled the trains and suffered with the Dust Bowl generation, the musical genius Woody Guthrie.

1b

1 two years of drought, years of overfarming and strong winds
2 poverty and unemployment, people became refugees and travelled around the country looking for work
3 Woody Guthrie

2

1 c
2 a
3 k
4 d
5 j
6 h
7 e
8 b
9 i
10 l
11 g
12 f

3

1 Because he also had experienced the effects of the Dust Bowl.
2 They are about the lives of real people and real situations.
3 He travelled by train because he didn't have any money and he could ride the boxcars for free and also because he found the life exciting.
4 There was only seasonal work and hunger and sickness were widespread.

4

1 Born in the American state
2 Living his early years
3 To escape the difficulties
4 Finding communication
5 To make matters worse for
6 Known as 'The Dust Bowl Troubadour'

5

1 Understanding what the film was about took us a long time.
2 Encouraging potential violinists to train with virtuosos is the aim of the project.
3 To make the observer feel calm and positive, he uses lighter colours
4 To be successful, the show will need to be financed by a wealthy sponsor.
5 Running in the West End for two years, the play made a profit of four million pounds.

6

Correct sentences: 2, 4, 5, 6, 7

7

1 clarity
2 harrowing
3 resonant
4 wailing
5 absurdities
6 suppress
7 chuckles
8 hardships

Unit 10 Lesson 3

1

1 b
2 b

2

1 Are video games a bad thing?
2 Two
3 Erica Winters

3

1 C
2 A
3 D
4 B
5 D
6 A
7 B
8 B
9 C
10 C

4

1 C
2 E
3 B
4 D
5 G
6 F
7 H
8 A

5

1 Showed you how to do it, didn't I? Easy.
2 The final conclusion was there wasn't enough funding to take a risk. That is to say they weren't prepared to take a risk without more funding.
3 Many people think there is no practical way we can make this work but I know we can.
4 Well, that's not the right way. I mean, we should do it more carefully like, for example, checking the location first.
5 We can print a picture, then write a poster on the computer and print it and then finally post them on every wall.

6

1 F
2 D
3 B
4 A
5 C
6 E

Unit 10 Lesson 4

1a

A and large
B Anyway
C kind of thing
D you know
E then again
F reckon that
G all in all
H That is
I before I forget

1b

1 F
2 C
3 H
4 D
5 A
6 G
7 B
8 I
9 E

Unit 10 Lesson 5

1

1 Identifying your role in the seminar.
2 Stating the topic of the seminar.
3 Making sure the scope of the seminar is understood.

ANSWER KEY

2a

1 what you're saying
2 running out of
3 see what you're
4 do you mean
5 balance
6 put it well
7 going back to
8 haven't heard from you
9 didn't catch that

2b

1 H
2 C
3 E
4 B
5 D
6 I
7 A
8 G
9 F

Unit 11 Lesson 1

1

1 imports and exports
2 mortgages and loans
3 supply and demand
4 assets and liabilities
5 creditors and debtors
6 income and expenditure
7 takeovers and mergers
8 boom and slump

2

a) 8
b) 7
c) 4
d) 3
e) 5
f) 2

3

1 level off
2 reach a peak
3 fluctuate
4 stabilise
5 surge
6 collapse
7 take off
8 plummet

Unit 11 Lesson 2

1

1 China
2 Brazil
3 Romania
4 South Korea
5 UAE

2

1 South Korea
2 China
3 China
4 Brazil
5 UAE
6 Brazil
7 Romania
8 China

3

a borrow – lend
b busted – boomed
c arisen – risen
d accept – except
e preceded – proceeded
f enquiry – inquiry
g credits – loans

4

1 accept
2 borrowing
3 bust
4 credit
5 inquiry
6 precedes
7 arose

5

1 UAE, China
2 Brazil
3 India

6

1 Raj
2 Sally
3 Raj
4 Danny
5 Raj
6 Danny

7a

1 provided that
2 unless
3 even if
4 But for
5 Supposing
6 whether or not
7 in case

7b

1 Even if
2 But for
3 unless
4 whether or not
5 supposing
6 provided that
7 in case

Unit 11 Lesson 3

1

Outside of the business world, another environment for negotiation is in the world of hostage-taking. This is what happens when a criminal uses innocent people as bargaining chips. It can happen in a range of circumstances, from a desperate mother who barricades herself in with her own child to terrorists who take foreign nationals. Fortunately for those who become hostages, there are professionals whose job it is to get them safely released. What do we need to know to be successful at hostage negotiation?

2

1 D
2 F
3 H
4 A
5 G
6 B
7 J
8 C
9 E
10 I

3

abolition
elimination
instigation
clarification
elimination
abstention
donation

confusion
decision
admission
permission
collision

4

1 clarification
2 elimination
3 abstentions
4 permission
5 donations
6 extension
7 instigation
8 admission

5

1 they have won
2 65 percent
3 three rounds
4 a goal, not a compromise
5 a big jump
6 too easy

6

1, 2

7a

talk about, go back, hand over, walk away , draw into, give up, leave with, speed up, slow down

7b

hand sth over, draw sth/sb into, give sth up, leave sb with (sth), speed sth up, slow sth down.

Unit 11 Lesson 4

1

- Liabilities
- Redundancies
- Debts and loans

2

1 C
2 E
3 D
4 G
5 H
6 B
7 A
8 F

3

Students' own answers

Unit 11 Lesson 5

1

1 At a sales meeting.
2 A sales representative, Evelyn Welsh.
3 The carry chair.
4 a) Introduction b) explaining product c) summarise / summary.

2

1, 2, 5, 6, 7

3

1 So, first of all, let me tell you where the idea came from.
2 For instance, they have those small umbrellas
3 So I've told you about the idea
4 To illustrate my point, look at the short film
5 I'll come back to that point later, if I may.
6 So, moving on now to the advantages.
7 I'd like to recap by saying that the Carry Chair is perfect for anyone
8 Thank you everyone for coming to my presentation.

4

Students' own answers

Unit 12 Lesson 1

1

1 astronomy
2 biology
3 zoology
4 geography
5 geology
6 chemistry
7 physics

2a

1 blossom
2 pollination
3 polythene
4 mercury
5 carnivorous
6 parasite
7 germinate
8 ridge

2b

1 germinate
2 ridge
3 polythene
4 parasite
5 pollination
6 carnivorous
7 mercury
8 blossom

Unit 12 Lesson 2

1

1 c)
2 a)

2

True statements: **4**, **6**, **7**

3

1 doubled
2 theory
3 misconception
4 reach Hubbert's peak
5 prediction
6 spell global recession

4

Students' own answers

5

1 ... more probable
2 The material is ...
3 it hasn't started yet
4 They can't have done
5 The best that we could find
6 If you close it
7 You failed to do so.
8 I think the family one would be better.

6

1 D
2 F
3 C
4 B
5 A
6 E

7

1 bother
2 had it up to here / anti-plastic brigade
3 the tree huggers / ranting
4 bonkers
5 spouting
6 is wheeled out

Unit 12 Lesson 3

1a Track 2.21

Just when you think that the lexicon of a language can do anything you suddenly find a huge hole. The English language is not that good at supplying collective nouns. There are the obvious ones like a group of grapes, a group of flowers. There are those that are a little more specialist, such as a group of geese, a group of wolves, a group of fish or a group of cattle. Yet, have you ever considered asking what the collective noun for bugs is? You probably know about a group of bees or a group of wasps. You may know of a group of ants. Yet there's nothing else. The latest suggestion on Twitter has been a bucket load of bugs. It's very descriptive I admit, but surely you can do better!

1b

bunch of grapes, bunch of flowers, gaggle of geese, pack of wolves, shoal of fish, herd of cattle, swarm of bees, nest of wasps, colony of ants

2

1 bedbug
2 globalisation
3 luggage
4 clothes
5 bites
6 the bed every
7 the exterminator
8 public transport, sit down
9 clothes / entering a bedroom
10 clean or dirty

3

1 stigma
2 infestation
3 stragglers
4 thrive
5 disembark
6 frisk
7 eradicated
8 slovenliness
9 hosts
10 slumbering

4

1 lines 54–55 David Cain advises …
2 lines 31–32 Bedbugs are hugely effective …
3 lines 36–39 with more and more …

5

1 B
2 C
3 A

6

1 C
2 E
3 A
4 D
5 B

7

Not mentioned: **2**, **3**, **5**, **6**

Unit 12 Lesson 4

1

1 Tropical insects will be the first species to become extinct.
2 a) pollination b) waste disposal
3 50
4 moving them into the shade

2

A said
B What / about
C If / correctly / suggesting
D if / pick up
E claims / suggesting
F regard / claim
G Perhaps / return

3

1 F
2 A
3 C
4 B
5 D
6 G

Unit 12 Lesson 5

1

1 g
2 h
3 f
4 b
5 i
6 e
7 a
8 j
9 c
10 d

2

1, 2, 6, 8